A TRIO OF PURSUITS

PUZZLES IN HUMAN DEVELOPMENT

To Janet, Leah, Jon, and James

Contents

———————⊙⊙⊙———————

About the Author

Professor Jerome Kagan is Daniel and Amy Starch Emeritus Professor of Psychology at Harvard University, USA. He is regarded as one of the fathers of development psychology, and was listed as the 22nd most eminent psychologist of the 20th century, out of more than 1 million psychology researchers worldwide. He is a Fellow of the American Academy of Arts and Sciences, a Fellow of the American Association for the Advancement of Science, and a member of the National Academy of Medicine. He has received numerous distinguished awards including the Hofheimer Prize of the American Psychiatric Association, the G. Stanley Hall Award of the American Psychological Association, the C. Anderson Aldrich Award of the American Academy of Pediatrics, the Wilbur Lucuis Cross Medal of Yale University, as well as Distinguished Scientist Awards from Society for Research in Child Development, Child-Mind Institute, and the American Psychological Association. He has served on numerous committees of the National Academy of Sciences, the President's Science Advisory Committee, the Social Science Research Council, the National Institute of Mental Health, and the National Research Council. He has written more than 20 books and hundreds of articles.

Professor Kagan was born in Newark, New Jersey in 1929. He was influenced by his grandfather's interest in the mind to pursue the field, and graduated from Rutgers University in 1950 with a bachelor's before earning his PhD from Yale University in 1954. He spent a year as a psychology instructor at Ohio State University before being recruited to work in the US Army Hospital during the Korean War from 1955–1957. His next destination was the Fels Research Institute, where he spent merely seven years as a researcher. Kagan accepted a professorship in 1964 from Harvard, where he has remained since.

Professor Kagan's research has centered on the cognitive and emotional development of infants and children. His highly respected and groundbreaking work especially focuses on the origins of temperament. At a time when most psychologists believed that personal characteristics were determined by environmental factors rather than by inheritance, he tracked the development of inhibited and uninhibited children from infancy to adolescence and discovered that shyness and other temperamental differences in adults and children have genetic influences. His pioneering results were revealed in his landmark first book *Birth to Maturity* in 1962. He has not looked back since, writing another 20+ books in the intervening six decades. *A Trio of Pursuits* is the final book of his exceptional career.

Preface

Descriptions of the three empirical efforts I regard as the most important in my long, satisfying career as a student of development comprise the content of this short book. Because most investigators hold a small set of premises that guide their investigations, an articulation of my convictions may help readers understand the questions I asked and the evidence my students and I gathered.

Some premises are traceable to childhood experiences in a modest, middle-class family in a city of 20,000 residents in central New Jersey during the depression of the 1930s. This setting made me acutely aware of the psychological properties that are linked to differences in social class, gender, ethnicity, and religion. As a result, I have always examined my data for the influence of these categories.

The small number of high school classmates who demeaned my Jewish identity generated the self-perception of an unwanted outsider, but this conception had the advantage of making it easier to pursue phenomena and offer hypotheses that were unpopular. Many years ago, psychologists at the University of California interviewed architects their colleagues had nominated as the most creative, as well as a random sample of successful, but less creative, architects. A perception of being ostracized by peers was more frequent among the creative group who commented that these experiences thickened their skin to criticisms by colleagues.

The origin of my habit of gathering as many measures as possible, rather than examining the relation between one predictor and one outcome, which is the usual strategy among contemporary psychologists, is more difficult to specify. I appreciated early that each source of evidence possesses some variance that is unique to that procedure and some that is attributable to a construct. Bohr's insight that no inference transcends its source of evidence implies that combining data from several sources promises to provide more valid conclusions.

I have always been suspicious of abstract, *a priori* concepts reflecting an investigator's preferences for how nature should be organized. Each time I read about the contents and functions of a human cell I am reminded of Haldane's insight that nature is queerer than we can suppose. Most of my empirical work was motivated by a puzzling observation that seemed to be a sign of an important issue. I was fortunate to have Frank Beach, a comparative psychologist at Yale who studied sexual behavior in varied species, as my mentor in graduate school. He was a joyful Baconian who often came into my small office and asked, "What might we discover today?"

A final premise is the product of an irrepressible desire to understand the mental properties of our species. Most natural scientists belong to one of two groups. A majority hope to illuminate a puzzle that is loyal to Peter Medawar's advice to pursue a problem that combines theoretical significance with amenability to measurement. The specific phenomenon is irrelevant. Had the cause of smallpox met those criteria in 1950, Crick and Watson might have chosen this question as their target of inquiry. These are the men and women who win Nobel Prizes.

A smaller group, who want to understand a specific species, phenomenon, or entity, understand that they might illuminate the phenomenon but leave intact most of its mystery. They are satisfied by lighting a candle in a dark forest. Some are intrigued by snow leopards, others by volcanoes. I chose psychology over biochemistry because the development of human thoughts and beliefs were the mysteries I felt compelled to understand. The wish to comprehend the bases of human prejudices was one reason for the selection of this target as a seminal curiosity.

Psychology as a field of study was popular in the 1950s. There was no pandemic and little concern with climate change, new sources of energy, or pollution of land and sea. Rather, some major worries were the prevention of crime and mental illness and understanding why children developed diverse personalities. It seemed obvious to many college seniors that psychologists, and especially those who studied children, would illuminate these puzzles. If the study of infants and children in laboratory settings were prohibited in 1950, I am not sure which career path I would have followed.

A Preview

The first four chapters of this narrative describe a trio of questions I asked together with the inferences that brought clarity to phenomena that continue to recruit the interest of scientists and the general public. The final chapter contains the lessons I learned over the past 60 years.

The degree of preservation of a psychological property from early to later life stages has been and remains a primary preoccupation of developmental scholars raised in Western Europe or North America. Asian scientists are far less concerned with this theme. The reasons for this cultural divide remain obscure. The ancient Greeks made things the foundation of all observable phenomena. The ancient Chinese awarded primacy to the complementary forces of *yang* and *yin* rather than to objects. Perhaps the severe natural catastrophes of flood and drought that were far more frequent in China than in Europe bent the Chinese mind to attend to the invisible energies that had such salient consequences. A flowing river, the most popular symbol of Chinese civilization, implies continuous change. By contrast, a solitary eagle is the symbol for America. Mandarin contains 20 verbs that describe the different ways an object can be held or carried, compared with the few forms in English.

Chinese philosophers, anticipating A. N. Whitehead by 2000 years, assumed observable events were the products of processes in flux rather than bounded entities with fixed properties. Listen to Confucius: "When the sun stands at midday, it begins to set / When the moon is full, it begins to wane." Western scientists have traditionally separated agent and object, true and false, good and bad. Chinese scholars merged these opposing ideas.

The European conviction to things as the basic entities made the permanence of the marks placed on a tablet a model for mind. 18th-century Protestant ministers regularly told their congregations that the biological mother's interactions with her infant imposed traits on the child that were preserved indefinitely. Listen to an 18th-century American expert: "Were man able to trace every effect to its cause he would probably find that the virtue or vice of an individual, the happiness or misery of a family, and the glory or the infamy of a nation have had their sources in the cradle over which the prejudices of nurse or mother have presided." [Smith, 1965]. A contemporary example of this position can be found in essays on the derivatives of a secure *vs.* an insecure infant attachment.

During the 1920s, several private American foundations funded longitudinal studies in different institutions. The Fels Research Institute in Yellow Springs,

Ohio was one site because Arthur Morgan, the president of Antioch College, persuaded Samuel Fels that families in southwest Ohio were less likely than those in Philadelphia, the headquarters of the Fels Foundation, to move from the area. Morgan's argument was successful and in 1929 the Institute staff began to enroll volunteer families with a young infant in a longitudinal project that, fortunately, gathered extensive descriptions of behaviors at home and in a nursery school at the Institute.

The Institute had received funds from NIH in 1956 to support a study of the relation between the behaviors displayed during childhood years and the traits possessed by adults who were now in their third decade. The Institute's director, Lester Sontag, who had offered the responsibility of directing this study to two different psychologists, was frustrated by their refusal. Fortunately, he remembered meeting me briefly in Frank Beach's office in the spring of 1954. This chance encounter is one of many improbable events that, in combination, sculpted my research career.

Sontag called me in December 1957 at the US Army hospital in West Point, N.Y., where I had been assigned after being drafted into the Army in 1955. He offered me the job that the other psychologists had rejected. With only two months before discharge and a return to civilian life I had been brooding on my career. I accepted his invitation to come to Yellow Springs to examine the corpus of evidence on the children. After seeing the extensive collection of data on each child from infancy to age 14 I recognized the opportunity to make a significant discovery, as well as the equally high risk of finding little of interest. Frank Beach warned me that if I chose the isolated setting of Yellow Springs, Ohio for the next five or six years my academic anonymity was guaranteed. I understood the risk but accepted Sontag's offer because of an intuition that the data contained some answers to the questions surrounding the preservation of traits and beliefs, which was one of the puzzles that I wanted to understand. Chapter 1, which affirmed my presumption, summarizes what my colleague Howard Moss and I learned.

The minimal predictability of adult traits from behavior during the first six years was one unexpected result that became the catalyst for a subsequent longitudinal study of infants conducted at Harvard soon after I joined the faculty in 1964. A second surprise in the analysis of the Fels corpus contributed 20 years later to the research on temperament described in Chapters 3 and 4. A small number of very timid two- and three-year-olds who consistently withdrew from the mildest threats became adults who were unusually dependent on others. Because this group did not differ from the rest of the sample in family environment, class, or gender, Moss and I entertained the hypothesis that these children were born with a temperamental bias. However, I did not pursue this idea until 1979 when other observations supported this possibility.

The study of infant attention to familiar and unfamiliar events in the first two years uncovered an unexpected U-shaped function between duration of attention to variations on human faces and age, with a nadir between six and eight months. This result implied that a new cognitive function emerged during the second half of the first year. Because Piaget's evidence on object permanence, avoidance of the visual cliff, and stranger and separation fear also appear between seven and nine months, I hypothesized that all these phenomena were the result of an enhancement of working memory that allowed older infants to retrieve schemata of past events while comparing them with the present event. The attempt to relate the two representations provokes prolonged attention or distress in some infants if the attempt fails. That is why many infants older than six or seven months cry to an unfamiliar adult and sudden departure of the primary caretaker in an unfamiliar setting.

These data implied the wisdom of initiating a longitudinal study of the second year with the hope of discovering patterns that had not yet been detected. Maturation of psychological properties was a popular target of study before the behaviorism of John Watson, B. F. Skinner, and Neal Miller dominated the empirical efforts of American psychologists. The insistence that the emergence of language and a moral sense were acquired talents, rather than inevitable products of maturational changes, had suppressed the study of this domain until the 1970s when a small number of investigators reported infant behaviors that appeared to be dependent on the lawful growth of the brain. Examples include the enhancement of working memory, length of a spoken utterance, imitation, and quality of play with a peer. Our work affirmed earlier suggestions that inference, language, a moral sense, and an awareness of self emerged in the second year. The evidence for these inferences is presented in Chapter 2.

The study of two infant temperamental biases, summarized in Chapters 3 and 4, had its origin in two different observations. I regularly brooded on the small group of timid three-year-olds in the Fels sample who became excessively dependent adults. A study designed to evaluate the effects of day care on infants, a collaborative effort with Richard Kearsley and Philip Zelazo, furnished a second reason.

The increased number of working mothers in the early 1970s created a demand for centers that would care for their infants during the day. The Nixon administration was considering a proposal to establish day care centers with government funds. But the majority of Americans in 1970 worried that the loss of maternal care for eight hours a day, five days a week, would generate problems in the children. Hence, an evaluation of the consequences of such care was obvious. We studied equal numbers of Caucasian and Chinese-American infants who attended our day care center or were reared only at home from three to 29 months. To our surprise, day care attendance had little effect on a varied set of measures. Ethnic group, however, did. The Chinese infants in both home and center groups were quieter, less active, and timider than the infants of European ancestry. This result, when blended with the Fels observation, made the study of temperament an imperative.

Chapter 3 presents our initial studies of a bold or avoidant style in young children. We found that the tendency to approach or avoid an unfamiliar, but innocent object, person, or setting was moderately stable over the childhood years. This observation led to a search for the origins of these habits in young infants. Chapter 4 contains the details of this effort. The evidence implied that the response to unfamiliar events in four-month-old infants defined two temperamental biases I called high and low reactive.

The final chapter contains a summary of new beliefs that gradually emerged from brooding on the results of all three investigations and the products of continual reading. The importance of examining patterns of measures, acknowledging the effect of the setting on the data gathered, and the distorting influence of semantic terms are the three ideas that became more clearly articulated in my later years.

Every writer imagines a hypothetical reader as a manuscript is being composed. Graduate students and younger investigators in psychology, as well as natural scientists who are curious about psychology, comprise my presumed audience.

I hope some readers find one idea that is as interesting as the many I have found in the books of others. I use she and he randomly in the text when referring to a single person in order to avoid writing she/he.

I am grateful to Robert Kagan, Marshall Haith, and Janet Kagan for wise comments on early drafts.

Chapter 1

What is Preserved?

———————— ⊙╳⊙ ————————

R eaders born after 1960 may find it difficult to comprehend the presumptions surrounding a child's development that were held by a majority of American psychologists during the first half of the last century. The high-status faculty in most psychology departments were studying rodents learning new habits in mazes and cages. The egalitarian ethos that has always been central to the American identity was a major foundation of the emphasis on learning. The country had to assimilate more than 35 million European immigrants who arrived between 1750 and 1920 and educate their children. This burden required a denial of biological differences and loyalty to the belief that the ideas, skills, and values acquired early in development were preserved indefinitely.

Geoffrey Gorer, an eminent social scientist in the 1950s, declared without embarrassment, "The habits established early influence all subsequent learning and, therefore, the experiences of early childhood are of predominant importance." [Gorer, 1955]. Thirty years earlier a psychologist wrote, "It is only the ignorant who take their babies to picture shows…they may show no signs of restlessness…or immediate symptoms, but some day the accounting must come — it may be in 20 or even 40 years later before it is paid in full, but paid in full it will be." [Fenton, 1925].

Faith in the indefinite preservation of habits, beliefs, and emotions contrasts with the ancient Chinese premise that nothing is permanent. This difference reflects a disagreement over the balance between the stability of childhood properties and the power of local circumstances to alter them. Many four-year-olds who are chronically disobedient become law-abiding adults.

The Concept of Attachment

Wordsworth's "child-as-father-of-the-man" lives on in writings on the consequences of the quality of an infant's attachment to the biological mother on adult personality traits. John Bowlby, a British psychiatrist, was certain that an infant's feelings toward and behaviors with her caretaker had lasting effects on her adult personality. Bowlby accepted the claim by Saint Ignatius Loyola, the 16th-century priest who founded the Jesuit order who penned a sentence that the behaviorist, John Watson, borrowed 350 years later: "Give me the child for the first seven years and I will give you the man."

The sorrowful wails of two-year-olds who had been left alone in a London hospital ward were one source of Bowlby's belief, even though his colleague at the hospital who reported this observation to him also told him that very young infants and children older than three years did not cry under the same conditions.

Several years later Bowlby observed the abnormal actions displayed by rhesus monkeys who had been separated from the mother at birth and reared on wire objects in Harry Harlow's laboratory at the University of Wisconsin. Bowlby ignored the fact that the monkey's behavior was more typical of the species if the wire object were covered with terry cloth or if the animal were reared with younger monkeys. Convinced that the relation with the mother in the first year established persistent emotional states, Bowlby published a series of books on the construct of attachment, the first in 1969 [Bowlby, 1969].

This book was followed by Erik Erikson's influential book, *Childhood and Society*, which announced that the infant's experiences with his parents determined whether the older child and adult would or would not trust others [Erikson, 1963]. Although neither Bowlby nor Erikson had any evidence to support their claims, the public's wish to believe in the validity of these declarations was sufficient. Neither Bowlby nor Erikson would smile upon learning that the parents of Paul Samuelson, a Nobel Laureate in Economics, and Gabriel Garcia Marquez, a Laureate in Literature, sent their sons away to be raised by friends or grandparents for their first seven years. Although both resented the separation, neither suffered from serious psychological problems and both men forgave their parents [Backhouse, 2017].

Bowlby recognized the need to find empirical support for his speculations. His former student Mary Ainsworth, who was now at The Johns Hopkins University, assumed this responsibility. Her students had observed the caretaking practices of a small number of Baltimore mothers with their infants. Mary needed a procedure that assessed each infant's quality of attachment to the mother. Because the reaction to the loss of the primary caretaker was the central feature of the attachment bond, she invented the Strange Situation. This procedure had the mother leave her infant temporarily on two occasions in an unfamiliar room, once with a stranger and later alone.

Because infants do not become upset by this incentive until the second half of the first year, Ainsworth tested one-year-olds. A mother and her infant came to an unfamiliar room at the University where the mother, on several occasions, got up and left the room and returned three minutes later. If her infant was crying, she tried to soothe the distress. The majority of infants cried but were easily quieted by the mother. A small number never cried and an equally small number were so distressed they could not be soothed.

Ainsworth and her students had to decide which pattern reflected a secure attachment and which an insecure bond. They decided that infants who were crying when the mother returned but were easily soothed had the most secure attachments. Infants who did not cry or those whose distress was so intense the mother could not soothe them were assumed to possess an insecure attachment. Ainsworth never considered the possibility that the infant's temperamental biases might explain their results, even though Ainsworth had entertained this idea several years earlier when she was observing infants in Uganda. Moreover, it was well known that some infants were especially susceptible to becoming distressed when left alone in an unfamiliar room [Arsenian, 1943].

When Ainsworth's results were published in 1978 [Ainsworth, Blehar, Waters and Wall, 1978], hundreds of young psychologists began observing one-year-olds in the Strange Situation, confident that they possessed a sensitive measure of an infant's attachment bond to a parent. None of these studies assessed the mother's behavior with her infant at home as well as adult traits to find out whether behavior in the Strange Situation did, indeed, provide the bases for a valid inference about the future.

A Critical Observation

My observations during a sabbatical leave for the 1972–73 academic year led to the publication of a paper with Robert Klein that questioned Bowlby and all who advocated the permanence of an infant's profile [Kagan and Klein, 1973]. I met Bob Klein while on a site visit to a research institute in Guatemala City. After the official visit ended he drove me northwest to Lake Atitlan, a large cobalt blue lake surrounded by a number of villages populated with descendants of the Mayan Indians. The small, poor, isolated village of San Marcos la Laguna seemed like a perfect place to observe children and parents in a non-Western context and satisfy a curiosity about the development of children growing up in a setting unlike any in the United States. I decided then to spend the year in this setting. My most important observation challenged the premise of the continuity of early traits.

Because the villagers believed that infants were vulnerable to the harmful influences following exposure to the gaze of strangers, especially men returning from work in the field, infants were placed in a hammock at the back of the small adobe home, without toys, until they could walk. The ability to walk was a sign of a newly acquired protection from harm. When these infants were allowed to emerge into the sunlight they were pale, frail, and unresponsive. American psychologists would have classified them as severely retarded. This persona contrasted with the properties of the five- and six-year-olds in the village who were active, laughing, and similar to the children I saw on Boston streets. Moreover, the cognitive tests we administered to older children implied levels of talent for inference and memory close to the norms for American children. It was obvious that the infant's psychological profile was not preserved over time.

Bob Klein and I believed this observation implied that a first year spent in a restricted setting that did not provide much variation in experience did not doom the child's growth, as long as the later environment furnished opportunities to regain the skills and cognitive talents that were inherent in the human genetic program. This claim was affirmed by investigators who had followed the development of children who spent less than two years in a depriving institution or suffered the privations created by the Second World War.

We were ingenuous. Bob and I failed to appreciate the Zeitgeist in America in the 1970s. The government had funded Head Start centers designed to provide the experiences that hopefully would allow poor children to attain the cognitive skills and regulatory mechanisms that were requisite for adaptation to American society. Many developmental psychologists worried that our paper would persuade Congress to reduce these funds because we wrote that a depriving first year need not create a permanently retarded person. These critics did not acknowledge that Klein and I were referring to the cognitive abilities that develop in all intact children, not size of vocabulary, familiarity with diverse facts about the world, knowing how to multiply fractions, or how to take a test.

Klein and I made one more attempt to shore up our position with later assessments of six- to 18-year-olds. Gordon Finley and Barbara Rogoff evaluated the use of rehearsal and semantic classifications in difficult memory problems in subjects from San Marcos and the larger, proximal village of San Pedro, which had a good school and organized economy. Elizabeth Nolan administered the same tests to children in Cambridge, Massachusetts. The evidence revealed that the San Marcos children acquired these memory skills later than those in the modern communities, but they did acquire them because maturation demands it. I will provide more details on this study in Chapter 2.

A majority of unschooled eight-year-old children from isolated villages across the world would attain low scores on the information and vocabulary scales of the Wechsler IQ test. But these same children would resemble Boston children on tests of short-term memory for the locations of four pictures of familiar objects, inferring an object from a few of its features, detecting the difference between physically similar, but not identical, objects, and suppressing a response to an incentive. These talents emerge in all children. Almost every child who is failing in an American school this year possesses these competences. But I did not have this evidence when I had to decide, in 1957, whether to take a job at the Fels Research Institute in the small Ohio town of Yellow Springs, midway between Columbus and Cleveland, or return to my earlier faculty position at Ohio State University before I was drafted in 1955.

The Fels Investigation

Few investigators in 1957 had conducted robust empirical tests of the premise that some traits were preserved from early childhood to the adult years. When Lester Sontag asked me to assume responsibility for implementing the NIH grant, no institution had behavioral observations on the same sample followed from infancy to adolescence that covered a broad range of traits. The Fels Institute did. That is why I accepted responsibility for this study. The task was to find meaningful relations between the childhood evidence and data to be gathered on the young adults willing to be participants once more.

Natural scientists and psychologists define preservation of a property in different ways. The former assumes an ipsative comparison in which an entity or a feature, whether an atom, molecule, gene, or cell, is compared with itself over time. By contrast, the psychologist studies comparative preservation of a trait in which each individual's score on a trait is compared with the scores of others in a particular sample. Frequency of crying decreases in almost all children over the first decade. But if each of 100 children retained the same rank for frequency of crying from one month to ten years, the coefficient reflecting preservation would be maximal at 1.0. This definition of preservation means that all conclusions depend on the sample studied. The preservation of a child's weight from birth to puberty will be higher in societies with high levels of income inequality than in those with minimal inequality. The Fels study assessed rank order stability.

The Sample, Setting, and Design

The sample consisted of 44 males and 45 females of European ancestry growing up in southwest Ohio during the depression of the 1930s. Although this group was not representative of Americans in 1957 or 2020, our results have not been disconfirmed by later work. Because the patterns we discovered have implications for contemporary efforts in psychology, a description of the study might be of value to this generation of psychologists.

The most important childhood evidence consisted of detailed descriptions of the behaviors of mothers and their children in the home, which were gathered semi-annually during the first six years and annually from six to 12 years. The children were also observed semi-annually at the Institute's nursery school from 2.5 to five years of age and annually from six to ten years. In addition, mental tests and interviews were administered several times on the children from age six to 14.

The only reasonable strategy for quantifying the childhood information was to invent psychological dimensions that could be rated after reading the behaviors described by the observers. Because behaviors change with age, separate evaluations were made for four intervals: infancy to age three, three to six, six to ten, and ten to 14 years. Howard Moss, who had just received his Ph.D. from Ohio State University, rated all the children for one interval before beginning the next. This decision minimized memory for the behavior of a particular child during the earlier stage. Fortunately, independent ratings by another psychologist agreed with Moss's ratings. The correlations between the two sets of ratings were in the .80s. Moss had no knowledge of the adult's traits.

I assumed responsibility for interviewing and testing the 71 adults who still lived in the vicinity and were willing to be part of the evaluation. I had no knowledge of their childhood traits. These data were gathered from 1957 to 1959 when the adults were between 19 and 29 years old. 28 percent had not attended college, 50 percent had some college, 22 percent were college graduates, and 70 of the 71 were Christian.

I interviewed each adult following a fixed order of questions. After listening to the taped recordings of the interview, I rated each subject on 44 variables on a seven-point scale. I also administered a variety of more objective procedures which I will describe when its evidence is presented.

What Did We Find?

The most significant result was the failure of the many behaviors Moss coded for the first six years to predict any adult traits. Prediction of adult behavior improved for the traits displayed from six to ten years with correlations ranging between 0.3 and 0.7. The one exception to this claim was a small number of toddlers, under three years, who consistently withdrew from novelty and mild threats and, as adults, reported a dependent relationship with a spouse or romantic partner.

One 22-year-old woman who was avoidant as a two- and three-year-old retained a timid persona as she developed. An observer at the Institute's nursery school noted that as a six-year-old, she rarely resisted the demands of a peer or seizures of toys in her possession. When teased she typically ran to one of the adults for protection. Two years later she was described as a "sensitive, delicate child who is both timid and nervous". The girl's mother told an interviewer that her daughter at age nine was "easily discouraged and hates to fail at anything". This girl became an adult who preferred to rely on her husband for all important decisions. She told me, "I have to have somebody to say — Yes, go ahead and do that…I don't like to do it on my own." This observation would become one of the reasons for my study of infant temperament 18 years later.

In contrast to the preservation of timidity in females, the preservation of forms of aggression and hostility from the school years to the adult years was significant for males but not for females. The child behaviors included open aggression toward the mother or peers, extreme levels of rage when frustrated, and excessive competitiveness with peers. The adult actions included verbal attacks on others and refusals to conform to another's requests.

One seven-year-old boy was described as "an impetuous child who was often malicious". He often destroyed the constructions of peers and would become enraged when frustrated. At age ten he deliberately made noise when walking, needled the teachers, and was "smug and sarcastic". As a 27-year-old he confessed, "I get irritated at drivers every day...I'm inclined to get too upset about things like that and be criticized for blowing up like that." He becomes angry when his wife reminds him to hang up his coat and later feels remorse for the outburst.

A second boy was equally aggressive toward peers, non-conforming to adult requests, and on one occasion at home squeezed a handful of newly hatched sparrows until they were dead. During a visit to the Institute at 12 years he had a "hangdog growl and a sullen expression". He confessed during the adult interview that he becomes openly hostile with his landlord and wife and believes that all humans feel hate.

The influence of gender on preservation of select traits was a third important finding. Preservation was enhanced when the trait was congruent with current sex role norms for each gender. That is why timidity to and avoidance of unfamiliarity during the school years predicted similar actions in adult women but not men. Not surprisingly, the women who had been timid girls preferred a job that promised financial security, even if the salary was lower than one involving more risk. Although sex role standards in 2020 are far less restrictive on females than they were in 1957, many contemporary women across 45 nations continue to have a stronger preference for a mate who can provide financial security over one who is physically attractive. Men hold the opposite bias [Walter *et al.*, 2020].

Gender Stereotypes

Most social scientists believe that the majority of observable sex differences in persona are the product of an acquired conformity to the culture's sex role standards. The comparisons all children automatically make between their features and those of select others create representations of the self that resist change. The establishment of a female gender identity is aided by the many occasions when school-age girls recognize that most boys are stronger, have more muscle mass, are more aggressive, more dominating of peers, and take more physical risks than a majority of females. This knowledge leads some female adolescents to select a domain of mastery that does not require competing with males.

Adults from different societies rated each of many nouns on the closeness of their association with one end of 50 pairs of antonyms that included big-small, strong-weak, heavy-light, nice-mean, good-bad, deep-shallow, and active-passive. Nouns referring to male roles or objects were rated as closer to the ratings for big, strong, and heavy than to their antonyms [Osgood, May and Miron, 1975]. The fact that, with the exception of Hinduism, most religious texts, written by men, refer to God, Allah, or a similar deity as a male makes it easier for boys to assume they should be dominant and for girls to accept a submissive role.

Biology

Although it is possible to explain the gender differences in usual behaviors as well as anxiety disorders and depression as due to historical circumstances that allowed men to dominate the community and dictate its norms, biological evidence makes some differences easier to understand. Strong claims about the biological contributions to the psychological differences between females and males are guaranteed to provoke strident controversy even though no difference applies to all members. A second caveat is more important. No difference, biological or experiential in origin, has implications for a society's laws or the person's opportunities to pursue any desired goal. A society can safely ignore any or all such differences without exacting a serious cost to its economy, power, or integrity. Women can be front line infantry and men can be nursery school teachers.

The sexes differ in genomes, anatomy, epigenetic marks, recombination at meiosis, parental origin of small changes in DNA called SNPs, brain chemistry, and immune response. The sex hormone testosterone, secreted by the male fetus, young infant, and adolescent, is a major contributor to a variety of sex differences that include muscle mass, skeleton, and brain. For example, this hormone prunes more synapses in the male than the female corpus callosum. As a result, the male's right hemisphere is freer from left hemisphere influences involving language.

The sexes also differ in the anatomy of the parietal lobe in ways that contribute to the male superiority on spatial reasoning problems and exceptional creativity in physics and mathematics that involve spatial relations [Salinas et al., 2012]. Furthermore, females have larger volumes in the prefrontal cortex and insula, sites that contribute to regulation of behavior and conscious feelings. By contrast, males have larger volumes in the occipitotemporal cortex, putamen, and cerebellum. These sites participate in object recognition, and motor actions. These sex differences are due mainly to variation in gene expression at these sites [Liu et al., 2020].

Although testosterone is the foundation of the male's primary sex features of penis and testes, a related molecule, dihydrotestosterone, is the basis for secondary male features that include a larger muscle mass, broader face, more prominent chin, thinner lips, and a shorter index than ring finger. The latter, called the 2D:4D ratio, is believed to be the outcome of the prenatal secretion of testosterone acting on androgen receptors in the carpal bones. Males with ratios smaller than .98 are more likely to be athletic, take more risks, and assume executive roles.

The amygdala is a major origin of autonomic arousal that generates conscious feelings with an unpleasant quality that are often interpreted as anxiety or fear. The fact that testosterone mutes amygdalar activity implies that males are less likely to experience the sensations that are interpreted as anxiety. The ratio of females to males with an anxiety or mood disorder is, currently, between 1.7 and 1.8 across 15 nations [Seedat et al., 2009].

In addition, the higher heart rate of most females may render them susceptible to anxiety. Each systole gives rise to a signal that arrives in the brain between 200 and 400 milliseconds later and resets the phase of the oscillatory patterns in many sites. This signal, called HEP, for heartbeat-evoked potential, activates the insular cortex which, in turn, generates a brain state that can generate a sensation that pierces consciousness and recruits the individual's attention.

The average woman has three systoles and three HEPs every two seconds compared with two for the typical man. In a ten-hour day marked by alertness, the typical woman has 54,000 HEPs compared with 36,000 for the male. Hence, it is reasonable to presume that these more frequent interruptions of brain states render females susceptible to psychological states they may interpret as worry, tension, or fear. American women with a diagnosis of social anxiety have larger HEPs than other women when told that their heart rate was rising [Judah *et al.*, 2018]. Finally, many studies report that women are more sensitive to pain than men and report higher levels of discomfort to the same painful stimulus [Mogil, 2012]. This fact would render females more likely to avoid situations that might lead to physical pain or psychological discomfort.

A Speculation

The corpus of evidence invites the following speculative account of the robust observation that more females than males, across culture and time, report feelings of intense worry and avoid situations that pose the risk of physical harm, loss of material resources, or criticism from members of their community. More females than males live with brain states that generate unpleasant sensations to mildly threatening or unexpected experiences. If the female interprets these feelings as reflecting anxiety, fear, shame, or guilt she is apt to search for its origin in her past. Because it is easy to retrieve a relevant cause, the individual becomes vulnerable to anxiety or guilt. The extensive collection of data on sex differences in varied animal species confirms the differences found in humans.

The gender differences in aggression have anlages in behaviors observed in infants and young children. A preference for playing with objects that move when manipulated, such as toy cars or trains, is more characteristic of young boys than girls [De Loache, Simcock and Macari, 2007]. Male rhesus monkeys have the same bias. Female rhesus prefer soft plush objects [Hassett *et al.*, 2008]. Seven-month-old infants first watched one adult cradle a balloon but another punch it. More boys imitated the adult who punched the balloon over the one who cradled it. The infant girls chose the latter response [Benenson, Tennyson and Wrangham, 2011]. Kicking and striking another are more frequent among boys than girls in most societies studied.

The biological differences between the sexes make it easier for diverse societies to preserve similar sex role norms. This claim does not imply that biology is destiny. A society can and often does advocate a norm that is inconsistent with biology because of an ethical preference that leads to greater civic harmony. Americans and Europeans in 2020 wish to minimize the contribution of biology to the traits that are more common in one sex. Humans are able to suppress many of the biases that originate in their biology. Whiskey has a bitter taste that infants find unpleasant but adults easily ignore their biology every time they sip scotch.

Concern with Academic Mastery

Variation in the motivation for high grades in school and enhancing self's knowledge during the school years predicted similar traits for both genders because sex role standards allowed their expression for males and females. The stability coefficients were equal for both genders and accounted for 40 percent of the variation in child and adult ratings. But unlike the prior two traits, the concern with cognitive skills was related to the education of both parents. These relations provided the highest correlations in the analyses, with some coefficients as high as 0.70. This relation between social class and intellectual mastery is as strong in 2020 as it was in 1957.

Social Class

The relation between the child's social class, indexed by parental education in the Fels sample, and the level of concern with school performance invites a more general discussion of the broad effects of class on a large collection of outcomes. Indeed, the social class of rearing is, in 2020, the best predictor of a serious illness, adult occupation, asocial behavior, cognitive skills, IQ, anxiety, depression, and inflammatory states [Sasser *et al.*, 2017].

Every known society invented criteria for relative rank in a community. Higher ranks were accompanied by greater access to resources, positions of power, and a sense of agency. The criteria chosen were often the abilities and traits that the society needed at the time. Skilled hunters, brave warriors, and pious clergy enjoyed the privileges of a higher class in earlier eras. Wealthy merchants, bankers, physicians, lawyers, and those with needed intellectual talents replaced the former during recent centuries. Many adults who did not possess the privileged criteria envied those who did and devoted their lives to acquiring the signs that allowed an ascent in class rank.

Class has two different, but related, meanings in contemporary research. Economists and sociologists prefer an objective index that combines income, education, and occupation. Psychologists often rely on a person's subjective judgment of their class position. The correlation between the two measures is modest; about 0.40 for white Americans but only .10 for African-Americans [Cundiff and Matthews, 2017].

The value of a college education was an important consequence of the industrialization of the 19th century. The more educated the parent, the more insistent their demands on the child to excel in school. Hence our finding of a correlation in the Fels sample between parental education and IQ scores and concern with the child's school grades is reasonable.

If one team of social scientists had access to 100 hours of film on each of 100 three-year-olds born in the United States in 1990 and a second team knew only their gender and the education of their parents, the latter would generate more accurate predictions of their adult occupation, marital status, mental and physical health, hobbies, and subjective happiness.

An Additional Discovery

One finding that became a catalyst for later work came from a test procedure administered on the adult's third visit to the Institute. I showed each adult three different arrays of cardboard figures taken from a popular test designed to reveal a concern with hostility, nurture, dependency, and sex. I asked them to sort the figures into as many groups as they wished based on one or more shared features.

The groups they produced fell into three categories. One was based on a shared physical feature, such as people lying down or those with no coats. A second category relied on a shared relation between or among several figures (e.g. a woman offering an object to another). The third grouping was based on a semantic name for a category, such as criminals, models, or angry people.

I was disappointed by the absence of any relation between each adult's groups and the childhood or interview evidence on them. Fortunately, I had recorded the response latency to each grouping. After many hours of examining the latencies I realized that the adults who generated many groups based on a shared physical feature took a little longer than those who produced few such groups. And the childhood evidence implied that the former were described by observers as more reflective in situations requiring a decision. This unexpected discovery led to a fruitful set of studies on the dimension I called reflection-impulsivity.

Most teachers notice the variation among school-age children in the time taken to choose one of several alternative responses on tasks in which the correct response is not immediately obvious. I decided to quantify this trait with a test that presented children with a target drawing of an object and beneath it five or seven variations that contained a single, subtle change in one feature that was not obvious at first glance. Children had to select the one variation among six or eight drawings that matched the standard. I called this procedure the Matching Familiar Figures test or MFF. A reflective style combines an above average response latency with an above average number of correct choices on the first response. An impulsive style combined fast latencies with many errors. The pattern of two measures was needed because some minimize errors despite fast response times.

A reflective or impulsive style in settings in which the subject believes his cognitive competence is being measured is preserved over several years in children who understand that a rapid response is more likely to be accompanied by an error. Most children less than six years have not yet acquired this idea. Hence the test is not appropriate. Second, each style is exploited in similar settings such as reading unfamiliar words, detecting a target embedded in visual noise, selecting via touch alone the one shape of many that matches a visual representation of a target, and recognizing scenes presented for short exposure times. The MFF test lost popularity when psychologists found that it did not evaluate behaviors in other settings, especially asocial acts in the child's life contexts.

Conclusions

The lack of predictability of the adult persona from the first six years, the interaction with gender and social class for select traits, and the small number of extremely timid toddlers who retained an avoidant style were the three main findings of our effort. Moss and I published our results in *Birth to Maturity*, which won the Hofheimer Prize awarded by the American Psychiatric Association [Kagan and Moss, 1962]. Had we found no relation between any childhood and adult trait our effort would have been dismissed as irrelevant to the issue of preservation because of insensitive methods applied to inadequate evidence.

If most physicists had held a skeptical view of Einstein's prediction that light from the sun would be bent by a small amount due to the sun's mass they would have dismissed Arthur Eddington's poor photographs of a 1919 solar eclipse as proof of General Relativity. Weak evidence is usually treated as support for an inference if a majority of scientists favor it. If an idea is unfavored it is difficult to persuade the investigators in a domain to treat excellent evidence as validating an idea. Papers claiming genetic contributions to psychological traits or mental illnesses that would have been rejected by editors in 1950 are published in high prestige journals in 2020.

The features that define acceptable social science in 2020 are a little different from those in 1957. Many contemporary psychologists would be critical of the practices Moss and I implemented. They would object to the fact that Howard rated the children for all three age categories because it raised the possibility that his ratings of the older ages were colored by memory remnants from earlier ages. The absence of minority group children would also be viewed as a serious deficiency. If I were 27 today, aware of the norms that dictate good science, and was offered the same job I took in 1957 I am not sure I would have accepted it. But the major conclusions have not been disconfirmed over the past 60 plus years. The success of the Fels project persuaded me of the value of longitudinal research on the same sample. The next chapter affirms that assumption for a different collection of concepts.

Chapter 2

Stages or Continuous Processes

———————◦†◦———————

Objects and processes change at varying rates. Attempts to understand the invisible mechanisms that mediate the changes usually assume one of two forms. When the rate is slow and gradual, as in the erosion of a rock, a continuous process is the preferred explanation. 18th-century scholars assumed the shape and organs of a newborn infant were present in a tiny form in the fertilized egg and simply grew larger over gestation in a process called preformation.

However, when salient changes occur over short intervals, say the emergence of a butterfly from a worm-like organism, most observers assume a qualitatively distinct collection of mechanisms that represents a stage of growth. Embryonic stem cells, which can differentiate into any body tissue, retain this potential for a very short interval of about four to five days after fertilization. Students of brain evolution during the first half of the last century believed that the human brain was a quantitative enhancement of the reptilian brain. That simple view is no longer held. The human brain is qualitatively different from the reptilian structure [Cesario, Johnson and Eisthen, 2020]. The thick band of fibers connecting the two brain hemispheres, called the corpus callosum, is present only in mammals.

However, continuous processes over long intervals, say the rusting of a bridge, can reach a tipping point that generates a discontinuous change when the bridge collapses. In addition, unpredictable events can create a qualitatively distinct pattern in what had been a continuous process. Examples include the meteorite that struck the region that is now Mexico 70 million years ago or an auto accident that paralyzed a person from the waist down.

There are qualitative differences between three-month-olds, three-year-olds, and 13-year-olds. It is difficult to defend the idea that the properties of the 13-year-old were products of the same processes operative in infants. Illiterate peasants in medieval Europe recognized, correctly, that the ability to assume adult responsibilities passed through stages with the seventh birthday defining a critical transition.

Many American psychologists resisted the idea of developmental stages after John Watson, impressed with Ivan Pavlov's discoveries, announced in the 1920s that no infant begins life with a biological program. Each child must acquire every competence by receiving a reward after making a correct response. Rewards for correct behaviors created and gradually strengthened each habit, whether babbling, walking, or speaking. This perspective dominated discussions of development for close to 40 years, until opposing evidence became so overwhelmingly inconsistent with its premises the burden of its defense became too heavy.

Observations of children in different cultural contexts furnished the most damaging evidence to Watson's views. Despite the distinctive variation in the behaviors that led to rewards, the milestones of grasping, standing, walking, speaking, and helping another appeared at roughly the same age in all settings. When neuroscientists measured developmental changes in brain anatomy and function, the case for stages became more convincing.

The First Two Years

The success of the longitudinal strategy at Fels persuaded me of the value of assessing the same sample of children over time. I implemented several longitudinal studies during the first two years after joining the Harvard faculty in 1964. Robert Fantz's work had indicated that it was possible for trained observers to reliably code the target of an infant's attention and Marshall Haith's studies of newborns confirmed the presence of preferences that were unlikely to be learned [Fantz, 1964; Haith, 1980]. Newborns as well as older infants look longer at stimuli containing contours and curvatures than at contour-free surfaces and linear contours. My studies of the first year focused on the variation in attention to varied events.

The Discrepancy Principle

Events that contain some of the features of a past event that had created a representation, called a schema, typically recruit the longest bouts of attention. Events that share no features with the infant's schemata, often called novel, recruit less attention because they do not engage an existing schema. Hence, there is an inverted U-shaped relation between the duration of attention to an event and the degree of difference between the agent's schemata for a class of events and the event in the perceptual field.

Most adults will devote more attention to a photo of a dog on a horse in the middle of a busy city street than to a spectrophotometer because the latter fails to engage a schema. There are many demonstrations of the validity of this principle in children from different cultural settings [Kagan, 1971; Wiener and Kagan, 1975; Kinney and Kagan, 1976; Finley, Kagan and Layne, 1972]. Many experiences that are labeled rewards are unexpected consequences of a response. Hence, they recruit attention and are accompanied by a phasic increase in dopamine which may strengthen the relation between the event and the behavior that produced it.

My students conducted a particularly convincing affirmation of the inverted U-shaped function. Four-month-old infants first saw 12 repetitions of a three-dimensional stimulus containing three meaningless elements. This object was called the standard. Infants were then assigned to one of seven groups. The mothers of infants in six of the seven groups showed her infant either the standard or one of several variations for 30 minutes a day over 21 days in the home. The infants in the seventh group saw no stimulus at home. Each infant returned to the laboratory at the end of 21 days where they were shown the standard object.

The infants who had been exposed at home to stimuli that shared some features with the standard, as well as those who saw no stimulus for the 21 days, displayed the longest bouts of attention. However, the infants who had been exposed at home to the stimulus that shared no features with the standard devoted minimal attention to this object, even though it had the most contour and largest variety of shapes [Kagan, 1971]. This inverted U-function between magnitude of difference between an event and the person's schema for similar events, on the one hand, and duration of attention on the other, has been replicated with variations on human faces, bodies, and other events over the last 50 years.

A Surprising Observation

A sample of 180 firstborn, white infants saw two- and three-dimensional versions of normal faces as well as variations that deleted the eyes or scrambled the features of a face when they were four, eight, 13, and 27 months old. I did not expect to find a U-shaped function between duration of attention and age with a nadir between seven and nine months. This observation has been confirmed with diverse stimuli [Courage, Reynolds and Richards, 2006]. Most infants devoted less attention to two- and three-dimensional versions of faces at eight months than they did four months earlier because it was easier to relate this event to their schemata for faces. But that process cannot explain the increase in attention to the same stimuli at 13 and 27 months. This observation implies a new stage of development.

A New Stage

The case for a new maturational stage in the middle of the first year finds support in a variety of phenomena that appear between seven and nine months. These include the ability to tolerate a longer delay before being allowed to reach for a hidden object, systematic scanning of the face and body of a human figure, avoidance of what appears to be the edge of a cliff, spontaneous imitation of actions seen one day earlier, and crying to the approach of a stranger or temporary departure of the primary caretaker in an unfamiliar setting.

In addition, infants acquire representations of the phonemes of their language around eight months [Kuhl, 1991]. These representations, called a prototype, are inferred from the sounds that recruit the infant's attention. Infants older than eight months no longer attend to changes in speech sounds that did recruit their attention when they were younger. For example, the Japanese language does not discriminate between the phonemes "ra" and "la". Although two-month-old Japanese infants orient to "la" after habituating to many repetitions of "ra", eight-month-olds do not because their prototype for the phoneme blends the two sounds into one. The older infants lost a competence they possessed six months earlier.

Distress to departure of the mother has been observed in infants from different cultural settings who experienced different rearing practices. Mothers from the Boston metropolitan area, Mayan villages in northwest Guatemala, the more cosmopolitan city of Antigua, villages in Botswana in southern Africa and rural Bangladesh, and an Israeli kibbutz left their infant temporarily in an unfamiliar setting. The proportion of infants who cried began to increase after seven months and peaked between ten and 15 months in infants from all seven settings [Kagan, 2013]. Reliable signs of distress to unfamiliar events appear between three and four months in monkeys, an age that corresponds to eight to 12 months in human infants. And puppies separated from their mother in an unfamiliar location begin to whine and vocalize at about three weeks of age, comparable to seven months in a human infant. These reliable facts imply that a new process emerges in the middle of the first year.

The Growth of Working Memory

These phenomena that appear after seven months can be understood if we assume that the older infants are able to retrieve and maintain schemata of events from the recent past and compare them with the present event. If they are able to assimilate the latter to the former, attention is terminated. If unsuccessful, however, some may cry because they cannot relate the event to their knowledge. One-year-olds in their home setting are more likely to cry when the mother leaves the infant by exiting from a door rarely used rather than a usual door [Littenberg, Tulkin and Kagan, 1975].

A study of eight infants tested every two weeks from six to 14 months affirms the growth in working memory during the second half of the first year. An attractive object was hidden under one of two cylinders followed by the placement of an opaque screen between the infant and the cylinders for delays of one, three, or seven seconds. No seven-month-old reached to the correct location when they had to wait seven seconds, but every 12-month-old did [Fox, Kagan and Weiskopf, 1979]. Nine independent studies found a linear increase with age in the delay infants could tolerate on similar tests of working memory [Pelphrey et al., 2004].

A procedure Piaget called the A not B error yields the same result. After infants have reached to the same correct location of a hidden object on four successive trials, the examiner hides the object at the other location while the infant is watching. The infant is allowed to reach after a varying delay. Eight-month-olds typically reach toward the previously correct place because of a failure to inhibit the rewarded habit. There was a linear increase between eight and 12 months in the probability of a correct reach as delays became longer. Eight-month-olds could not tolerate delays longer than three seconds while one-year-olds were successful under 20-second delays [Diamond, 1990].

The enhancement of working memory after seven months is due to maturational changes in the brain, especially increased connectivity between temporal, parietal, and frontal cortices, as well as structural changes in dendrites on pyramidal neurons in region CA3 of the hippocampus [Reyes *et al.*, 2020]. Since unexpected or unfamiliar events typically activate the basolateral amygdala, which has reciprocal connections with the hippocampus and prefrontal cortex, it is relevant that these connections become stronger between eight and 12 months as a result of myelination of axons within the internal capsule [Chrousos and Gold, 1999].

The Second Year

The discovery of an enhanced working memory during the second half of the first year motivated an examination of the second year in the hope of finding the appearance of psychological processes other than speech which was a frequent target of inquiry. Most children begin to talk in the second year, but there is a sharp disagreement on the origins of this ability.

Language Acquisition

One group, for whom Noam Chomsky is the hero, argues that humans possess functions devoted only to language that allow children to acquire the grammar of their language with minimal effort. The opposing view acknowledges that evolution awarded humans a vocal apparatus that was lower in the throat and specific brain sites tuned to the properties of speech that made speech and its comprehension easily acquired skills. However, many believe that the other mental processes needed for language are not restricted to this competence. These general functions include the ability to infer the intentions of others, notice physically salient sounds, orient to discrepant events, maintain words and schemata in working memory, and detect low-level correlations between contiguous events.

Detection of correlations between contiguous events allows infants to separate continuous speech into separate words. The sequence p-r-e is followed by t-t-y with no delay 80 percent of the time when English-speaking adults direct speech to infants. But the sequence t-t-y is followed by b-a with no delay less than one percent of the time. Hence it is easy for children to learn that pretty is a word but ttyba is not [Saffran, 2003].

The automatic tendency to attend to an unexpected event leads children to notice unfamiliar words or vocal emphases. By the end of the first year most infants are ready to associate the sounds of speech with objects and events. No other species finds this process so easy to accomplish. Deaf children learning a sign language display semantically meaningful signs at the same age as hearing children.

Most linguists agree that the 6000 current human languages possess properties denied to other species. The ability to communicate meaningful messages to members of the same language community that contain references to objects or events that no one has experienced is one such feature. English speakers who are familiar with Lewis Carroll's works will extract meaning from the following sentence: "The ghost of the Mad Hatter's unicorn, who had been sleeping in an angel's halo for millennia, suddenly emerged in the form of a snark looking for a boojum."

Young children rely on three biases while acquiring a first language [Markman, 1992]. They assume a spoken word refers to a whole object rather than a part. Van Quine, one of the most respected philosophers of the last century, denied this bias. He argued that a visitor to a society that spoke a language he did not comprehend would not know what the word "gavagai" meant if spoken by a native who pointed to a rabbit moving across a meadow. Gavagai could refer to the animal's ears, head, whole form, or movement. However, almost all two-year-olds would assume that the strange sound referred to the whole rabbit.

The assumption that a word refers to a collection of similar objects is a second bias. Children hearing gavagai upon seeing a rabbit will assume that this word refers to all animals with the shape and coloring of a rabbit. A bias of exclusivity leads young children to the incorrect assumption that each object or event has only one name. If an adult usually uses the word "apple" when naming this object, but one day later says "Let's eat your fruit", the child will be puzzled. Fortunately, older children lose this bias.

Most nouns have less ambiguous meanings than a majority of verbs because a number of languages allow a verb to be used with distinctive nouns. Examples in English include the verbs eats, sleeps, breathes, reproduces, moves, and kills, which can be used with sharks, snakes, vultures, chimpanzees, and humans as noun agents. Some languages, Russian is an example, alter the verb with an inflection that implies the noun agent.

The ambiguous referents for the agent which is common for many English verbs has had a profound influence on theory in psychology because its major constructs are functions, often named with verbs, rather than things. Psychologists write about the predicates fear, learn, or remember in sentences in which the agent is not specified. When biologists write about mitosis colleagues know that the noun is a cell.

Three Additional Processes

The initial stages of a moral sense, inference, and a conscious awareness of self were less common targets of study in the 1970s. The published research on these themes was scattered across specialized journals read mainly by those interested in one of these phenomena. No psychologist to my knowledge had tried to detect the properties shared by language, inference, morality, and self-awareness. The possibility of finding this prize motivated a longitudinal investigation of the second year. The samples in the seven studies we conducted consisted mainly of children from Cambridge, Massachusetts, but included subjects from other cultures on whom measures of language, working memory, inference, symbolic play, and imitation were gathered.

Inference

I begin with inference because it contributes to the other three processes. Obviously, it is necessary to specify what is inferred. Ten-year-olds infer a broader range of representations than two-year-olds. We assessed the ability to infer the referent for a spoken word and the intention of an unfamiliar adult. A female examiner asked the child to infer that an unfamiliar word probably was the name of an unfamiliar object. After a practice trial to acquaint the child with the situation, a toy doll, dog, and irregularly shaped styrofoam were placed in front of the child. After allowing the child to play with the objects she asked "Give me the zoob" or "Give me the iboon" on alternate monthly visits to the home.

Most children, whether from Cambridge or a village on one of the Fiji islands, began to make the correct inference by the middle of the second year and by 26 months every child gave the examiner the styrofoam.

One of my doctoral students provided a stunning demonstration of an enhanced inferential talent during the early months of the third year. Children 18, 27, and 36 months old were visited in their homes where they played either with a pair of clear ski goggles that allowed sight or a pair of opaque goggles that blocked visual perception. One day later each child-mother pair came to a room in our laboratory. After the child had played for a while, the mother put on the opaque goggles. Only the 27- and 36-month-olds who had prior experience with the opaque goggles inferred that the mother could not see. These older children tried to remove the goggles and were surprised when the parent asked for objects in the room that presumably she could not see. Some 36-month-olds asked her to take off the goggles so she could see the room. Neither the 18-month-olds who wore the opaque goggles at home nor the older children who had experience with the normal goggles displayed these actions [Novey, 1975].

The ability to infer the psychological state of another makes empathy and cooperation possible. Children now show a concern upon seeing an adult display signs of pain that was absent during the first year. The ability to infer distress in another is one basis for the universal moral prohibition against inflicting harm on an innocent victim. Some social scientists have argued that the ability to cooperate is one of the important traits that make humans unique. However, neither children nor adults would cooperate if they were unable to infer the trustworthiness of the other.

The child's behavior in one of our laboratory procedures implied a blending of inference with an emerging understanding of a moral obligation. Children from 13 to 36 months initially played with a set of toys for ten minutes while the mother sat a few feet away on a couch. A female examiner entered and she and the mother joined the child on the floor. The examiner modeled three different but complex actions with multiple toys, accompanied by a narrative describing what she was doing. She then said, "Now it's your turn to play." She did not say or do anything to imply that the child was obligated to imitate her actions. Hidden observers coded the child's play for the next ten minutes.

More than 40 percent of the children who were 18 months or older began to cry, fret, or cling to the mother as soon as the examiner stood up to leave. This behavior was observed in samples from Cambridge, Winston-Salem, North Carolina, Fiji, and children of recent immigrants to United States from South Vietnam. When one parent reminded her son that he was to play, he went to a corner of the room where he began to sob. A two-year-old girl insisted on going home while throwing toys against the door.

The display of uncertainty to the simple request by an unfamiliar adult to resume play reflects a blend of language, inference, moral sense, and self-awareness. The child had to understand the meaning of the examiner's phrase, infer that she wanted the child to imitate her actions, feel an obligation to do so, and be aware of an inability to honor the inferred obligation to imitate a sequence that was too difficult to remember.

In order to eliminate some alternative explanations we ran a procedure in which the adult did not say "Now it's your turn to play". Few children cried under this condition. Nor did crying occur when the unfamiliar adult did not model any actions but only played with the child. Finally, crying was minimal when the mother displayed the same acts and uttered the same phrase. Distress only occurred when an unfamiliar adult modeled the actions because most young children assume they ought to obey requests from strangers in a laboratory. The Eskimo of Hudson Bay believe that two-year-olds have acquired *ihuma*, meaning an awareness of the ability to know which behaviors are and are not appropriate.

A child's identification with a parent or family, an insufficiently studied process that emerges by the fifth birthday, requires the child to infer that she shares select features with a parent. When this inference is combined with a feeling that the child interprets as pride or shame we say the child has an identification with the parent. A child who has an identification with a parent assumes, incorrectly, that others will treat him as if he possessed parental features that he does not have. These properties can be desirable or undesirable.

The more distinctive the parent's features, the stronger the identification. Similarity in gender or an unusual physical or behavioral feature is always important. The Israeli writer Amos Oz had a prideful identification with his famous father who was a writer. John Updike's identification with his father, on the other hand, was accompanied by shame. He writes in his memoir, "I would show them, I would avenge all the slights and abasements visited on my father — the miserly salary, the disrespect of his students, the laughter in the movie house at the name of Updike." [Updike, 1989, pp. 32].

A few years later many children establish identifications with their social class, ethnicity, and/or religion. Autobiographies reveal that the intensity of pride or shame linked to these identifications has a profound effect on adult mood and behavior. Norbert Weiner confessed to feelings of inferiority due to his identification with the ethnic group called Jews.

Self-awareness

The child's speech in the home setting supported the emergence of an awareness of self by the middle of the second year. Children now began to issue directives to the parent to behave in particular ways. One 18-month-old gave a telephone to the mother saying "Do it". Several months later she gave the parent a doll and toy bottle and indicated by gesture that she wanted the parent to feed the doll. These directives to the parent were correlated with the child describing what she was doing at the time. For example, one girl said "up" as she tried to move her body on to a couch. Others used "I" in utterances such as "I go", "I do", or "I play". One 26-month-old said "I step on my ankle" and "I do it myself".

Similar observations by others imply that as children become consciously aware of their ability to use their body to attain desired goals they simultaneously comment on these acts [Bloom, 1973]. Self-corrections of speech, which emerge late in the second year, and the use of words referring to internal feelings, which appear in the third year, also imply components of self-awareness [Kristen et al., 2012].

Children older than 16 months who are facing a mirror touch their nose if their mother had surreptitiously placed rouge on it, implying an awareness of self's body [Lewis and Brooks-Gunn, 1979]. This index of self-awareness is present in most children by the end of the second year. Karl Sabbagh remembered that when he was about two years old he first had the insight that he was a person. "I was sitting on a stool…my father was reading to my older brother and I felt left out…it was I who was frustrated." [Sabbagh, 2009, pp. 13–14].

Although most authors of papers on consciousness, a synonym of self-awareness, assume the term refers to one brain and psychological state, it is more likely that the varying targets of consciousness are accompanied by slightly different states. A conscious desire for chocolate, love, fame, friends, or sleep evokes different feelings, schemata, and semantic networks. Therefore, it is improbable that the psychological and brain states accompanying these desires are identical, even though all may share activation of one of the neuronal ensembles that accompanies each state. The premise of a single state of consciousness is facilitated by the fact that English, but not all languages, has only one word for consciousness.

The human brain has a larger number of distinctive, spindle-shaped neurons, primarily in the anterior cingulate and fronto-insular cortex, than any other mammal. These sites are believed to mediate conscious feelings, control of impulsive responses, and immediate detection of errors in motor actions. Older adults with select forms of dementia have fewer of these neurons, called von Economo neurons. This observation implies that these neurons contribute to states of consciousness that every healthy 20-year-old possesses.

Human Morality

Every known society invents a list of praiseworthy and prohibited behaviors and labels its members good or bad depending on their loyalty to the standards on these acts. Physically harming an innocent, damaging another's property, deception, and dishonesty are prohibited in all known cultures. The moral prohibition against causing physical harm to another can include acts that create hurtful feelings. The recent prohibition of public expression of comments that demean the members of a group that have been victims of past prejudice has become, among many tolerant Americans and Europeans, a reason to ostracize anyone who dares to ignore this imperative. No one is allowed to speak or write in ways that generate deeply unpleasant feelings in those who have been victims of persistent and unjust prejudice. The geneticist James Watson is among the prominent Americans who have been removed from the list of the admired for failing to honor this ethical demand.

The human moral sense emerges in the second year when children have established prototypes for the usual appearance of objects and the behaviors of others. Damaged objects and acts that cause distress in others are violations of these prototypes. Children in the second year say "yukky" or "bad" when they see a flawed object and infer the likely cause of the flaw. Because parental punishments generate distress, children infer that similar actions will create unpleasant feelings in others. The ability to infer the private thoughts of others and exposures to adult punishments for certain actions lead children to label violations of family norms bad.

The Need to Contextualize a Moral Prohibition

Many philosophers and social scientists search for a universal set of moral prohibitions that transcends all settings. These usually include imperatives against killing another, restricting a person's freedom, or ignoring the distress of another. These declarations are indifferent to the agent, the victim, and the context. The moral status of any action, however, must be contextualized. The elders of a Gusii tribe in Kenya did not punish two men who killed their mothers because the men said that their mothers were witches [Ogembo, 2001]. A 13th-century Spanish law allowed a man, who was obligated to a noble to defend a besieged castle, to eat his child if he were very hungry, rather than surrender, unless the noble relieved him of this responsibility. Abraham was willing to kill his son Isaac in order to remain loyal to God.

A citizen of Costa Rica who usually stops to help a disabled stranger cross a street in San Jose is less likely to perform the same altruistic act when in New York or Karachi [Levine, 2003]. American loyalty to the moral idea of personal freedom made a major contribution to its rise to dominance. However, the conditions generated by the COVID-19 virus require Americans to give up some freedom and obey government demands to wear a mask in public. The fact that many refuse to abandon their commitment to personal liberty affirms the influence of the historical setting on the persuasiveness of a moral standard. These and other observations affirm the powerful effect of the setting on the honoring of a moral belief. The failure to specify the agent, act, target, and context explains why scholars are still arguing about the definition of morality.

Every economic system presumes an ethical standard that favors some beneficiaries over others. American economists during the first half of the last century assumed that a *laissez-faire* capitalistic economy with limited government intervention was the best arrangement. They did not acknowledge that its premises rested on moral beliefs centered on personal freedom. Hence, they were initially not receptive to John Maynard Keynes's 1936 book that urged government intervention to smooth out the highs and lows in an economy. This belief was so strong in 1948 that several members of the Governing Board of MIT were angered by Paul Samuelson's support of Keynes in his recently published textbook. One member accused Samuelson of being a Communist. These businessmen would have been outraged by the decisions of the 2020 Congress to give trillions of dollars to small businesses and individuals during the COVID-19 crisis. Each new law also presumes an ethical standard that awards one beneficiary more importance than others. Should the individual, the family, the community, all nations, or the planet possess the privileged position?

John Rawls [1971], whose popular book on justice awarded priority to the less advantaged, admitted 20 years later that his position would appeal mainly to liberal, 20th-century citizens of North America and Scandinavia. Pre-Enlightenment scholars insisted that neither reason nor empirical evidence demanded equal distribution of material resources.

The Importance of a Private Conscience

The historical events that replaced the moral authority of village elders, clergy, or a deity, which imposed a conformity on all members of a community, with each individual's private judgement was enhanced in Europe during the 11th century. As a result, society had to add a new term to name the feeling that pierces consciousness when the individual took responsibility for violating a standard he accepted as obligatory. English selected the term guilt to name the interpretation of this feeling. Shame, by contrast, is the salient emotion in those living in communities in which almost all are loyal to the same norms. An adult from an isolated village in Kyrgyzstan told an anthropologist, "If you do not follow others, it is not good." [Beyer, 2016].

The Later Years

Maturation and experience after the second birthday extend the breadth of the moral sense. Four-year-old children from diverse cultures insist that the allocation of rewards to members of a group that worked on a common task ought to be proportional to the person's contribution to the effort. No other primate displays evidence of an appreciation of fairness. The argument favoring equity over equality in the distribution of material things or access to power is one exemplar of a more general human preference for a proportional relation between events. Large objects make a louder sound than small ones when they fall. Large wounds require more time to heal than small ones. Punishments for serious violations of a moral code are more severe than the punitive practices following minor misdemeanors. These and thousands of similar experiences create a prototypic schema of proportionality that applies to the relation between the amount of effort a person expends during a task or the level of skill applied to a problem and the magnitude of reward the person ought to receive, whether money, status, or access to power. That is why citizens of many nations oppose laws that allow governments to send money to disadvantaged adults who are not required to do anything in return.

A few five-year-olds in one of my studies refused an examiner's request to tear up her favorite photo, despite their compliance to ten prior requests that did not involve a moral standard. One boy explained, "No, it's your favorite photo", implying a reluctance to be the cause of her unhappiness. What began in the second year as the ability to infer select thoughts in another became, by the seventh birthday, an automatic blame of the self for failing to honor beliefs that had been accepted as obligatory. A mother in one of my studies found her three-year-old son, who was ostracized by peers because of his aggressive behavior, pinching himself with a force that caused pain. His reply to the mother's question as to why he was inflicting pain on himself was "I don't like myself".

The psychological state of the typical seven-year-old who has violated a moral standard depends on a blend of three conditions. The belief that one harmed another for any reason is the first. Children insist that teachers can require obedience to many rules, such as code of dress or seating arrangement. However, they cannot enforce a rule that requires imposing pain or discomfort on another. Such behaviors are always wrong [Shweder, Turiel and Much, 1981]. The belief that one is responsible for imposing distress on another is the second. This decision varies across persons for it involves a judgment. A few Norwegian parents whose children survived a shooting incident on Utoya Island on July 11, 2011 told an interrogator that they felt guilty because they did not do something to prevent the trauma from occurring [Thoresen, Jensen, Wentzel-Larsen and Dyb, 2016].

Adults who adopt a moral standard that prohibits an emotion or behavior that is a common product of human biology are susceptible to guilt. Jealousy is one such emotion. The British psychologist, Stuart Sutherland, who had decided that jealousy violated his personal standard because it was irrational, fell into a guilt-induced depression when he was unable to suppress intense jealousy upon learning that his wife was having an affair with his best friend [Sutherland, 1976].

The belief that select others will privately disapprove of self's acts is the final condition. O. H. Mowrer, a famous American psychologist in the 1950s who committed suicide at 75, wrote, "You are your secrets." The combinations of these three beliefs determine whether the child or adult experiences only empathy or a blend of guilt, shame, and empathy following the recognition that the self did something that harmed an innocent.

The Guatemala Research

Although all children with an intact brain possess the capacities described in this and the prior chapter, they vary in the age at which they appear as function of the environmental support of their expression. I noted in Chapter 1 that I was eager to confirm the validity of this idea in 1972 when I spent a sabbatical leave observing children and adults in the small, Mayan village of San Marcos nestled on the shore of Lake Atitlan in northwest Guatemala. The evidence gathered by many students over the next seven years affirmed the intuition that the time of appearance of select human cognitive talents depends on the setting.

Studies of children ranging from four months to 16 years revealed that Mayan children developed the basic talents of selective attention to discrepant events, an enhanced working memory, inference, language, moral standards, and a keen awareness of their personal agency, feelings, and thoughts. But the age when these competences appeared was later and the rate at which they improved was slower than in Boston children.

Infants from Cambridge, Massachusetts and San Marcos saw two different visual sequences several times before seeing a discrepant variation on each sequence.

The American infants had longer fixation times than the Mayans but the slopes of looking times over trials were similar in both groups. Infants five to 21 months from San Marcos were compared with children from an adjacent, more modern town of San Pedro which had a larger, better educated population that engaged in varied businesses. The attentional patterns to discrepancy, working memory, and the symbolic play of San Marcos children lagged behind the children in San Pedro and Cambridge by several months. But the San Marcos children showed improved performances on all three tasks as they matured. Crying after the mother and examiner suddenly left the child alone (in the home in San Pedro and San Marcos but in the lab in Cambridge) occurred at eight to 12 months for all three groups.

The more complex cognitive competences measured in children between five and 12 years also grew more slowly in San Marcos children. The abilities to recall and recognize many previously seen familiar objects and infer the name of an object from a few schematic lines matured earlier in Cambridge and San Pedro children. But the slopes of improvement over age were similar for all three samples [Kagan and Klein, 1973; Kagan, Kearsley and Zelazo, 1978].

The last assessment of the Mayan samples evaluated the ability to hold many items in working memory. The San Pedro and Cambridge samples ranged from six to 13 years. The San Marcos group ranged from six to 21 years. Children had to remember the locations of drawings of 12 familiar objects, the orientations of 12 identical dolls, and recall the names of a set of familiar words. A description of the first task provides a model for the doll procedure.

Initially each child saw a row of pictures of familiar objects. The pictures were then turned over and the child had to remember their locations. If the child was correct with two pictures, the memory burden was increased to three pictures. Each time the child was correct an additional picture was added. The final score was the number of pictures whose locations were remembered. Days later a variation on the above task with the same 12 pictures was administered. Now the child first saw a sequences of two to 12 pictures and named each one. The examiner then turned all the pictures over and while the child was attentive she changed the location of one or more pictures. The child had to reproduce the altered sequence. With each correct response the number of pictures and number of alterations were increased.

The data resembled those described earlier. The scores of the San Marcos children were lower than those in San Pedro and highest in Cambridge. But the slopes of improvement in working memory were identical in all three samples. As expected, the children of parents in San Marcos who could speak and read Spanish, wore shoes rather than sandals, and had a few more years of education had the best memory scores. A family's status in a community, whether Los Angeles, Singapore, or San Marcos, has similar effects on the cognitive skills and motivation of their children.

One observation confirms the importance of the specific information to be remembered in memory tasks. A sample of 20 eight- to nine-year-old San Marcos children were asked to learn associations between each of 20 meaningless designs and a different familiar word. 15 of the 20 successfully acquired these 20 associations after only six repetitions. They were then given sequences of three to seven of these designs representing three to seven words and had to read the sentence the sequence symbolized. Two examples were: "The dog sits" and "A boy sits in a canoe". Eight-year-olds who could not remember the locations of four pictures learned the 20 associations and read the sentences correctly. Apparently learning the concrete referent for an unfamiliar stimulus, which is required for acquiring a language, is friendlier to human biology than the less natural task of holding in working memory separate schemata for the locations of unrelated pictures [Kagan, Klein, Finley, Rogoff and Nolan, 1979].

A final study compared the recognition memory of five-, eight-, and 11-year-olds from Cambridge with children of the same ages who lived in poor, subsistence farming villages in the eastern part of Guatemala. Each child saw 60 pictures of common objects taken from American magazines that were familiar to American children, but many were unfamiliar to the Guatemalans. Recognition memory was assessed immediately, one day later, or two days later by asking the child to pick the one picture in a pair he had seen earlier. Although the five- and eight-year-old Guatemalan children had lower scores than the Americans, the cultural differences were minimal by age 11 [Kagan, Klein, Haith and Morrison, 1973].

Brain Growth

The fact that inference, language, a moral sense, and self-awareness emerge during the same developmental interval implies new forms of brain organization. The evidence, although slim, affirms this possibility. The length and branching of dendrites do not approach adult values until the second birthday [Schade and Ford, 1973]. The rate of decrease in neuronal density (number of neurons per unit volume) slows early in the second year when the cortical layers assume a similar form [Rabinowicz, 1979].

Of special relevance is the growth of neurons in cortical layer three which is accompanied by much faster transfer of representations between the two hemispheres [Mrzljak *et al.*, 1990]. Now the schemata of the right hemisphere are more quickly combined with the semantic networks in the left. This change makes comprehension and longer utterances easier and by facilitating the blending of schemata with language it enhances the ability to infer another's psychological state. Finally, lipids used in myelination of axons from the cerebellum, which controls muscular movements in speech, do not reach mature levels until the second year [Martinez and Ballabriga, 1978].

The evidence implies a qualitative change in functions rather than a quantitative enhancement of the competences of the first six months. The 20-month interval between display of the first smile to a face and the declaration "I can't do that" when faced with a difficult task marks the emergence of a collection of properties that distinguishes humans from every other species.

The Future

As the final assessments of the two-year-olds were being completed I was composing a book-length summary of a collaborative study of the effects of day care on Chinese-American and Caucasian infants. The obvious ethnic differences in avoidant behavior between the two groups, which I describe in the next chapter, evoked a memory of the small number of avoidant one- to three-year-olds in the Fels sample who retained derivatives of this trait as adults.

These diverse observations generated more frequent brooding on the concept of temperamental biases that made it easy or difficult for a child to acquire select traits. I had resisted this possibility because of my desire to believe that experiences were the major determinants of variation, a belief supported by the psychologists at Yale during my graduate years in the early 1950s. But by 1979 my reluctance to acknowledge biology had dissipated and temperament had become an acceptable target of inquiry because of the growing popularity of biological contributions to psychological differences. I was now ready to implement my own probes of this concept. The next two chapters describe this work.

Chapter 3

Behavioral Inhibition

————————⟡⟡⟡————————

I noted at the end of the last chapter that my prejudice against a major biological contribution to variation in behavioral profiles was challenged by the obvious differences between the Chinese and Caucasian infants in our study of the effects of day care during the 1970s. A brief summary of this research explains why the evidence required acknowledging the influence of biologically based temperamental biases on select behavior patterns.

The Day Care Study

The pressure on Congress to establish federally supported day care centers in every state was growing during the 1960s as more women with young children entered the workforce. Many developmental psychologists opposed this legislation because of the unproven belief that the experiences of the first two to three years shaped a child's future personality. Bowlby's strong statements on the importance of an infant's attachment to the mother provided a scaffold for the conviction that the biological mother ought to be the primary caretaker during the opening years. It seemed useful, therefore, to test this popular idea.

Richard Kearsley, Philip Zelazo and I were granted funds by NIH to implement a study of the consequences of day care on black infants living in a working-class neighborhood of Boston. Unfortunately, a group of leaders in the black community feared that any study of black infants by white professors would be harmful to the population they were protecting. They demanded that we terminate the research. Happily, a pastor of a church in Boston's Chinatown promised to protect our day care center from harassment if we enrolled some children from his district. NIH agreed to the change in the sample and we enrolled healthy infants born to Chinese-American or Caucasian working- or middle-class mothers. One group of Chinese and Caucasian infants attended a day care center we administered up to eight hours a day, five days a week located in a working-class neighborhood and staffed by both Chinese and Caucasian women. A second group of Chinese and Caucasian infants from the same class and neighborhood were raised only in their home setting.

Both day care and home-reared infants were assessed eight times between 3.5 and 29 months with procedures designed to measure variation in attention to violations of the familiar, emotional states, social interaction patterns, reactions to separation from the mother, and age-appropriate cognitive skills. Interested readers can find descriptions of these evaluations in our 1978 book *Infancy* [Kagan, Kearsley and Zelazo, 1978].

There were minimal differences between the day care and home-reared children in cognitive skills, but obvious ethnic differences in behaviors and biology that implied the influence of temperamental biases. The Caucasian infants from both groups vocalized and smiled more often and had more variable heart rates than the Chinese. The latter observation triggered a memory of a result on the Fels sample that I did not understand at the time. The small number of Fels adults who had preserved a timidity they showed as toddlers displayed less variable heart rates at rest than the other adults in the sample. Low heart rate variability implies a stronger influence of the sympathetic over the parasympathetic nervous system on the heart.

We coded each child's response to temporary separation from the mother on every assessment. More Chinese than Caucasian infants fretted or cried on each of the five assessments from eight to 29 months in both the day care and home-reared groups. However, there were no ethnic differences in selective attention to the mother when, at 20 months, the mother, a caretaker for those in day care and a familiar adult for the home controls, and an unfamiliar woman suddenly rose and changed chairs on two separate occasions in an unfamiliar room. Almost all the children looked at or went to their mother following these unexpected moves. This observation implies that the bond to the mother was stronger than the one to the familiar woman at the day care center who cared for the infant. The final evaluation at 29 months included a visit to an unfamiliar day care center with the child's mother. The Chinese children from both groups remained close to their mother for a longer time. These observations implied the possibility that the Chinese and Caucasian infants possessed different temperamental biases. Before describing our forays in this domain, a brief history of this concept is useful.

Conceptions of Temperament

Every culture has a preferred explanation of the variation in the personas of its members. The most common account attributes the variation to a balance between experience and inherent qualities. The contrast between the ancient Greek and Chinese cultures provides an example. The Greeks favored the influence of each person's bodily substances, called humors, while acknowledging the influences of diet and climate. Hippocrates, a Greek physician who dealt with the material symptoms of illness, argued that the balances among the properties of blood, yellow bile, phlegm, and the mysterious black bile were the foundation of psychological traits.

The Chinese awarded more power to environmental forces that required each person to accommodate to the frequent changes in their ecology. Each change altered, temporarily, the balance between the complementary energies of *yang* and *yin* from which each person's source of energy, called *qi*, emerged. Because the environment was unstable, each individual's level of *qi* was not preserved indefinitely. The frequent occurrences of floods, droughts, and plagues of locusts, which had profound effects on families in an agricultural society, seemed to originate in forces rather than things. Hence, the preference for the energies of *yang* and *yin* rather than the relative stability of the properties of blood, phlegm, and bile.

Because the Greeks had a far greater influence on psychology than the Chinese, their ideas dominated scholarly treatises on temperament. Galen, a second-century physician who elaborated Hippocrates's assumptions, posited nine temperamental biases derived from blends of the four humors. Individuals blessed with the four ideal temperaments had a perfect balance between the qualities warm and moist, features of the blood humor, and the qualities cool and dry, properties of black bile.

When one member of a pair was dominant, the four less ideal temperaments called sanguine, melancholic, choleric, and phlegmatic were expressed. Because spring is wetter and warmer than winter a sanguine temperament dominates. The cooler, drier autumnal months enhance melancholy. These concepts, with slight additions or deletions, remained popular until the end of the 19th century.

The Chinese, by contrast, who placed the balance of power in local settings, assumed change was inevitable and emphasized the importance of education. This early difference in the balance between the individual and the setting is preserved in the cinemaphotography of contemporary film directors. Americans and Europeans film many close-ups of one or two persons in which the context is absent. Asians typically include the setting in which characters are acting.

The introduction of behaviorism in the 1920s, which trivialized each person's biology at a time when Americans were trying to integrate millions of European immigrants, rendered an initial blow to all temperamental concepts. Hitler's declaration a decade later that Aryans were born with a biology that implied a temperament superior to all others made research on temperament unpopular for about 40 years.

A number of events resurrected the legitimacy of inherited contributions to patterns of behavior. New discoveries in genetics following the Crick and Watson 1953 paper on the structure of DNA had a profound influence. Dissemination of the Thomas, Chess and Birch claim of nine temperaments was also important, although they studied mainly Jewish infants born to faculty at a New York university and relied on parental descriptions of infants as the primary evidence [Thomas, Chess and Birch, 1969].

Studies of intra-species variation in behaviors implied that some members of every vertebrate species had a disposition to approach novel or unexpected events while others withdrew, even though the genetic foundations for these biases were not always the same across species. For example, puppies belonging to different dog breeds raised at the Jackson Laboratories in Maine watched their handler slowly walk toward them and eventually pick them up. Terrier pups were timider than cocker spaniels.

Some guppies in a large vessel with a large predator fish swim toward the latter, while most remain far from the large fish. In time the predator has eaten all the bold guppies while the timid ones survived. But female guppies prefer to mate with the bold males. The cost of an abbreviated longevity is balanced by a reproductive advantage.

When strain or species differences in timidity to an unexpected event were found to be correlated with variation in neurochemistry, the case for temperaments became more persuasive [Kagan, 1994]. Human brains contain more than 150 different molecules and more than 2000 different receptors for these molecules. Individuals vary in the concentrations of the molecules as well as in the density of the receptors at varied brain sites. For example, humans vary in the density of mu-opioid receptors in varied brain sites [Kantonen *et al.*, 2020]. Adults with more mu-opioid receptors in the thalamic neurons that transmit pain are likely to experience less pain than those with fewer receptors. If each genetic origin of a molecule or receptor that contributed to a temperament had five alleles there could be as many as 3×10^{750} possible temperamental biases, far more than the nine proposed by Thomas, Chess and Birch.

Definitions of Temperament

Contemporary scholars do not agree on a definition of temperament or the source of permissible evidence. This level of dissent confuses readers who are new to this literature. My definition, which has not been accepted as the most useful, is at least concise. I view a temperament as an inherited pattern of brain chemistry or anatomy that contributes to the likelihood that the child will experience certain feelings and acquire or display certain behaviors that usually appear during the first few years of development. Some of the behavioral signs of a temperament include excessive or minimal irritability, ease of soothing when upset, smiling, regularities in appetite or sleep, activity level, and reaction to unfamiliarity. When environmental events, such as negligence, prematurity, or season of conception, are the bases for display of these traits, the behavioral profile ought to be given a distinct label to distinguish it from an inherited pattern. At the moment this separation is not honored because investigators do not know how to separate the different origins of the same responses.

The source of evidence for a temperamental bias should always include behavioral observations and, when possible, biological measures as well. Verbal descriptions of a child's behaviors or moods are not sufficiently sensitive predictors of behavior unless supplemented with direct observations. No natural science relies only on expert knowledge as the bases for its facts or constructs. Empirical studies affirm or refute experts.

Questionnaires

The majority of studies of temperamental biases in infants or adults rely on a person's answers to a questionnaire. There are good reasons for its popularity.

Fierce competition for research funds and tenured positions at universities force young investigators to publish many papers each year. This need motivates investigators to select inexpensive procedures that can yield a lot of data in a short time. The cost and time needed to gather, code, and analyze behavioral evidence make it difficult to meet the pragmatic goals the current academic context demands.

The investigators who rely only on questionnaires ignore or deny the many factors that restrict all inferences to this narrow source of evidence. The correlations between parental reports on their children, on the one hand, and observed behaviors are not sufficiently high to allow investigators to assume that the former are sensitive indexes of the constructs inferred from behavior. That is why Hill Goldsmith and his students developed a procedure for infants and children that relies on observed behaviors to varied incentives to assess nine traits that might rest on a temperamental bias [Gagne *et al.*, 2011].

The limitations trailing answers to questions are easy to describe. First, the questions have to use a vocabulary that is comprehensible to all informants and evoke similar networks of semantic forms and schemata. A parent who activated images of her child throwing objects randomly when frustrated will probably affirm the query "Is your child angered by frustration?", while a parent who evoked images of her child sulking for a few seconds is apt to say "No" to the same question. A mother in one of our studies who had described her three-year-old daughter as highly sociable with peers confessed surprise when, watching through a one-way mirror, she saw her daughter's shy, timid behavior with a pair of three-year-old girls.

The content of the question affects answers. When preadolescents were asked to name the events they feared most, a majority chose spiders. But when the children were given a long list of potentially feared things, burglars and being unable to breathe were named far more often than spiders [Muris *et al.*, 2000]. The particular word used affects the replies. Adult members of identical and fraternal twin pairs (MZ or DZ) filled out a questionnaire asking about tension in settings with strangers. An affirmative answer to the statement "It is hard for me to start a conversation with strangers" was heritable. But an affirmative reply to "I feel nervous if I have to meet a lot of people" was not [Horn, Plomin and Rosenman, 1976].

Questions for parents have to refer to events that almost all parents notice. This means that the investigator cannot ask about the occurrence of subtle or brief responses, such as increases in blinking, brief frowns, or changes in the tension of the muscles in face or body that films can reveal. Finally, children as well as adults resist reporting the possession of properties they regard as undesirable. Many Latino and black adolescents from poorer families living in southern California denied their compromised social rank as they matured [Rahal *et al.*, 2020].

It remains possible that the vocabulary parents use to describe their child's behavior and the constructs investigators invent to represent the results of a frame-by-frame coding of child behaviors in varied settings are incommensurable. That is, the words a parent uses to describe her child's fear of attack cannot be replaced with the terms that describe the facial and body muscles that change when a child anticipates being attacked by a peer.

Continua or Categories

The choice between temperamental biases that reflect continuous variation in magnitude and categories of children that are limited to those with extreme values is a second issue warranting discussion. The work to be described implies that children who withdraw from and cry to many unfamiliar events and settings are qualitatively different from the larger number who show timidity to only a few incentives. Only ten percent of two-year-olds in one sample were consistently shy and timid across a variety of unfamiliar events [Rubin *et al.*, 1997].

The current preference for continua is facilitated by the statistical procedures taught in graduate schools and the preferences of reviewers and journal editors. These procedures work best on continuous distributions. Fewer analytic techniques are designed to detect categories of children or adults. The tail wags the dog. The frequency and amplitude of EEG signals in a sleeping adult form continua, but the pattern of frequency and magnitude observed in REM sleep is regarded as a qualitatively distinct category.

If ten percent of children in a sample of 1,000 possess values on three measures that are in either the lowest or the highest five percent of the distribution, and there is no correlation among the variables for the remaining 90 percent, correlations among the three measures for the whole group will be non-significant, even though ten percent of the children share high or low scores on all three measures.

Our First Studies

Because I have always favored a Baconian empiricism over tests of *a priori* hypotheses, I chose to observe variation in signs of hesitation or avoidance to unfamiliar events and settings as the target of inquiry rather than the concepts of fear or anxiety. But in 1946 psychologists assumed that hesitation to or retreat from an object or situation reflected a fear state. The eminent psychologist Donald Hebb was among this group [Hebb, 1946]. Developmental psychologists had observed, but had not yet explained, the reasons for the variation in hesitancy of approach, crying, or seeking proximity to a parent when confronting a stranger. I assumed that temperamental processes were likely causes of the variation in these behaviors for the children who fell into either extreme on a dimension that had extreme timidity at one end and extreme boldness at the other. I called the former type inhibited and the latter uninhibited. I shall use INH for inhibited children and UNIH for those who are uninhibited.

I had read that rats conditioned to become immobile to a cue that signaled electric shock to the paws possessed an activated amygdala that sent projections to the central gray which led to the immobility called freezing. The similarity between an animal's immobility and an inhibited child's prolonged hesitancy to approach an unfamiliar object implied that the genes responsible for the variation in the excitability of the amygdala might contribute to the biases to approach or avoid unfamiliar events.

Cynthia Garcia Coll, a graduate student looking for a project for her Ph.D. thesis, assumed responsibility for the initial effort. She filmed the behaviors of 117, 21-month-old Caucasian, middle-class children born at term. She restricted the sample to white children because of research implying ethnic variation in genomes that could influence temperament.

Each child encountered four different violations of their past experience in an unfamiliar setting with their mother present. She measured heart rate and heart rate variability because of evidence implying a relation between a timid bias and reduced variability in heart rate as well as larger accelerations to unexpected stimuli. I present detailed descriptions of the subjects, the procedures, and the coded variables that defined the constructs we called INH and UNIH because readers cannot evaluate the validity of our conclusions if they do not know the evidence on which the inferences were based.

Initially a woman implemented the procedure described in Chapter 2 in which she modeled complex actions with toys and then said to the child, "Now it's your turn to play." After the child recovered from any distress and the examiner had left, an unfamiliar woman entered, sat on a chair, and using the child's name invited her to play. The woman then left the room and the first woman returned, went to a corner of the room, uncovered a metal robot, and invited the child to approach and touch the metal object. The woman then left the child and mother in the room. Several minutes later, on a signal, the mother rose and left the child alone for several minutes. After the mother returned and the child was calm the pair went to a room where the child's heart rate and variability at rest and to scenes were measured.

Variation in withdrawal from the unfamiliar events, time spent near the mother, amount of speech, time playing, and crying were the most common signs of INH behavior. These variables, along with latencies to approach the unfamiliar events, were combined to create an index of an inhibited or uninhibited response to the unfamiliar. An examination of the distribution of scores suggested break points that separated the 28 percent of the sample (33 children) with very high scores (INH children) from the 31 percent (38 children) with very low scores (UNIH children). The remaining 41 percent had less extreme scores. Children with extreme values on a measure often display greater preservation of a trait than those who have less extreme scores [Kagan, Reznick and Gibbons, 1989].

These children returned several weeks later to experience the same sequence of episodes. Fortunately, most children retained their category assignment, especially those with extreme values. Further, INH children had lower heart rate variability at rest and larger heart rate accelerations to discrepant events [Coll, Kagan and Reznick, 1984].

Nancy Snidman, who joined my laboratory as Cynthia was completing her work, wanted to do spectral analyses of the heart periods of each temperamental group in order to assess differences in vagal versus sympathetic tone on the heart. She observed an independent group of 31-month-old children because a spectral analysis requires the subject to be motorically still and older children are better able to suppress movement. Nancy had to choose different procedures because Cynthia's events were not sufficiently novel for 31-month-old children. We had learned that the behaviors displayed upon confronting an unfamiliar child of the same age and gender were sensitive signs of an INH and UNIH bias to the unfamiliar. After 30 minutes of play with a peer, a woman wearing a plastic cover over her head entered, remained silent for several minutes, and then invited the two children to approach her. Measures of time spent close to the mother, frequency and latency to initiate play with the peer, amount of spontaneous talking, and latency to approach the woman with the cover were used to compute indexes of the response to the unfamiliar. 15 percent of the sample (26 children) were unusually shy and timid (INH) and 14 percent (25 children) were extremely sociable and bold (UNIH).

The INH and UNIH children from the two samples were pooled and observed at four, 5.5, and 7.5 years of age in settings in which the mother was always with her child. Behavior with an unfamiliar child provided the index of inhibition in four-year-olds. Four different incentives furnished the evidence for the index at 5.5 years: behavior with an unfamiliar peer, latency to explore three novel objects in a small room, behavior in the child's kindergarten classroom, and amount of spontaneous speech during an hour with an examiner who administered varied cognitive tests.

The 7.5-year-olds were observed in two procedures administered on different days. The child's behaviors with seven to ten unfamiliar children during a 90-minute session of free play and competitive games provided one source of evidence. The frequency of spontaneous comments with an examiner as well as the latency to utter the first six comments comprised the second index.

The Findings

The variation in behavior in the child's kindergarten at 5.5 years affirmed the stability of each bias. The children who had been INH earlier were more subdued, solitary, and wary than those who had been UNIH. One girl classified as INH at

21 months retreated from a peer with whom she had quarreled and screamed whenever any child approached her. After several minutes she crawled under a table and stared at her classmates engaged in activities. No UNIH five-year-old expressed such unusual actions.

The INH 5.5-year-olds shown a picture of a fearful and fearless child while listening to a description of the scene looked longer at the fearful child. The INH also attended to the passive rather than the active member in 13 pictures of dyads in which one person or animal was the active agent and the other was passive (e.g. one animal approaches another lying down, an adult points a finger at an immobile adult, an animal is chasing a child). The UNIH five-year-olds were more likely to look initially at the active agent. Finally, the mothers of INH five-year-olds more often reported that their child had a fear of storms, swimming in the sea, going to bed alone, fires, robbers, and being kidnapped. Psychiatrists who had interviewed the parents in Cynthia's sample found that 18 percent of those with INH children had social anxiety disorder compared with no parent of an UNIH child.

Variability in the level of tension in the muscles of the larynx also differentiated the two groups of five-year-olds. The muscle tension is inferred from the variability of the pitch periods in spoken words. The lower the variability the greater the muscle tension. The vocal utterances of INH five-year-olds had less variability.

The INH children also had higher concentrations of the stress hormone cortisol in their saliva across three samples obtained in the morning. We computed an average z score across eight biological measures gathered at 5.5 years, which reflected activity in sympathetic targets or the hypothalamic-pituitary axis. This score was correlated with the index of inhibition at 21 months ($r = 0.70$). 67 percent of the children who were INH at 21 months had high values for both biological activity at five and an INH patten at seven years. By contrast, 65 percent of UNIH children had low values on these variables [Kagan, Reznick and Snidman, 1988].

Over three-fourths of the children from the Arcus and Snidman samples first seen at 21 or 31 months preserved their behavioral category at 7.5 years. When the criterion for INH or UNIH was limited to children with extreme values on the behavioral index (0.6 standard deviations above or below the mean), one-third of the children retained their earlier temperamental category and only three toddlers had changed categories. The majority had moved from one of the extremes to the middle of the distribution and were neither INH nor UNIH at seven years.

An independent group of 100 children observed at 14, 20, 32, 48, and 66 months in unfamiliar settings displayed similar levels of preservation of each bias [Kagan, Reznick and Gibbons, 1989]. The mother of one seven-year-old INH boy described the primary feature of her son's personality. "If something is new and different his inclination is to be quiet and watch…It's unfamiliarity that is the cause of his behavior…it has to do with newness."

The Assessment at 13 years

The assessments of the 13-year-olds classified as INH or UNIH at 21 or 31 months consisted of one session with an unfamiliar examiner who administered tests and a later interview with Carl Schwartz. The amount of spontaneous speech and frequency of smiling with each of the unfamiliar adults were the most distinguishing features in the two settings. One-half of the sample preserved their temperamental bias and only 15 percent had acquired the persona of the contrasting category. This result affirms the earlier claim that a temperamental bias influences the ease of acquiring and preserving certain behaviors. An INH or UNIH profile at one year does not guarantee preservation of the profile because older children can, with effort and a supporting environment, suppress the urges favored by their temperament. Inhibited American boys experience more teasing and bullying than girls with the same persona, making an INH profile a greater risk for later problems in boys than girls.

One INH boy I shall call Tom displayed a pattern shown by the more extreme INH youths. Tom had been the most inhibited child at every assessment from 21 months to age seven and had a high value on the biological index at five years. This boy had a tall, thin body build and a narrow face, which characterized about one-quarter of the INH boys. Tom sat stiffly on the front of his chair for most of the interview, occasionally biting his lip or twisting his hands together. His face remained impassive and his replies were terse. His grades placed him in the top five percent of his class in mathematics and English. He told the interviewer that he wanted to be a scientist because "I like thinking about problems". When a relative died he began to worry about the possibility of his parents dying in an automobile accident.

Ralph, also a firstborn boy born to professional parents, was among the three most UNIH males at every assessment. Ralph was talkative and had low scores on almost all of the biological measures. Ralph had a mesomorphic body build, a relaxed posture with no small motor movements, and treated the interviewer as if he were a peer. He also had good grades, wanted to be a professional drummer in a band, and could not remember any fear that lasted for more than a week.

A Pattern of Physical Features

Many INH children shared Tom's tall, thin body frame, narrow face, and blue eyes. The higher proportion of blue eyes in the Caucasian INH children and their relatives was an unexpected observation. Allison Rosenberg asked the teachers of 133 kindergarten or first grade classrooms to nominate the shyest and the least shy Caucasian child in her classroom along with their eye color. In this New England sample of 266 children, 43 percent had blue and 41 percent brown eyes. However, 60 percent of the extremely shy children had blue eyes (versus 42 percent of the minimally shy) and 58 percent of the sociable children had brown eyes (versus 40 percent of the shyest children). Allison's observations of the behaviors of 35 children were correlated with the teacher's assessments [Rosenberg and Kagan, 1989]. Others have reported a similar result [Coplan *et al.*, 1998].

It may not be a coincidence that artists in the Walt Disney studio were more likely to give blue eyes to characters who were vulnerable to fear, such as Pinocchio, Dopey, and Cinderella, but award dark eyes to less anxious characters, such as Grumpy, Peter Pan, and Cinderella's stepsisters [Arcus, 1989]. Strains of rats with a dark coat color (called non-agouti) are tamer than those with a gray coat (agouti) and foxes with a darker coat color are less avoidant of unexpected events than those with a lighter coat. Rainbow trout with many dark melanin spots on the skin have a less responsive hypothalamic-pituitary axis to challenges [Kittilsen *et al.*, 2009]. The binding of melanocortin molecules to one or more of the five receptors, which affects the darkness of coat color, affects the animal's vulnerability to stresses, energy level, and sexual and aggressive behavior [Ducrest *et al.*, 2008].

More UNIH youths shared Ralph's muscular build and broad face. Chief executive officers of companies listed on the Dow Jones or a comparable German index had broader faces than the average male or female in that nation [Hahn *et al.*, 2017]. Even school-age children rely on this facial feature to judge a person's competence and electability to a public office [Antonakis and Dalgas, 2009]. Capuchin monkeys with a broad face are more often the alpha animal in the troop [Lefevre *et al.*, 2014]. Dog breeds with a tall, thin body frame, defined by the ratio of the standing height at the shoulder divided by the cube root of the animal's weight, are more timid than dogs with a mesomorphic body shape.

The combination of a tall, thin body, narrow face, and blue eyes is found most often in northern European populations. The climate in this region 30,000 years ago when humans arrived was very cold. Because the thermoregulatory mechanisms of the new arrivals were set for warmer temperatures, any mutations that allowed improved preservation of the body's heat would be adaptive. Genes that increased the amount of fat would have helped, but this change did not occur. Mutations that enhanced the excitability of the sympathetic nervous system are a second possibility. If some northern Europeans acquired genes that were accompanied by higher levels of norepinephrine or corticotropin-releasing hormone, they would enjoy faster, more effective constriction of the skin's capillaries, which, in turn, would prevent the escape of body heat. At least one study conformed this assumption [Maley, Eglin, House and Tipton, 2014]. However, the chemistry that mediates this adaptive feature also lowers the threshold of activation of the amygdala. As a result, these individuals are more susceptible to feelings that can be interpreted as worry or fear.

We were surprised by the higher prevalence of eczema and hay fever in the INH children and their first- and second-degree relatives. Higher concentrations of cortisol could contribute to this relation. This molecule increases the level of immunoglobulin IgE, which releases the contents of mast cells in skin and respiratory tract to produce the symptoms of eczema and hay fever.

The sympathetic ganglia, adrenal medulla, melanocytes, and facial bone are all derivatives of neural crest cells which appear early in the embryo's growth and migrate at about four weeks post-fertilization to affect eye color, facial shape, and the sympathetic nervous system. Furthermore, the neural crest may contribute to the greater prevalence of the allergies among HR children. The T cells that affect susceptibility to an allergy mature in the thymus. The neural crest is the origin of one set of thymic cells, called stromal, that secrete a cytokine which can contribute to an allergy of the skin or respiratory tract [Maroder, 2000]. It is tempting to speculate that changes in select genes in northern Europeans 30,000 to 40,000 years ago altered neural crest cells in ways that led to some of the prototypic physical features of the INH child.

The indexes of INH or UNIH behavior did not predict either IQ or a host of specific cognitive abilities. However, more INH children were more risk averse. INH 5.5-year-olds who were free to set the distance between themselves and a basket into which they were supposed to throw a ball chose a shorter distance than UNIH subjects. The 13-year-olds were asked to imitate an examiner who had fallen backwards onto a soft mattress. Most UNIH youths adopted a free, unrestrained fall with their heads striking the mattress. One-third of the INH fell cautiously to a sitting position.

The genetic contribution to INH or UNIH behaviors finds support in several studies. The most persuasive was conducted a decade ago at the University of Colorado. The sample consisted of 178 same sex, mainly Caucasian twin pairs (356 children) observed at 14, 20, 24, and 36 months in a laboratory setting during which behaviors during tests and play sessions were observed. The MZ twins were far more similar in display of extremely shy, cautious behavior than the DZ twin pairs. The heritability coefficients ranged from .58 to .87 across the four laboratory assessments [Emde and Hewitt, 2011].

The entire corpus of observations, along with the work of others, implied that the preferred reactions to unfamiliar or unexpected events might have genetic bases [Fox *et al.*, 2005]. Discovery of the infant predictors of INH or UNIH children would quiet the critics of temperament who argued that behavioral differences in the second year could be the product of prior experiences. The next chapter describes this effort.

Chapter 4

High and Low Reactive Infants

————————⊙✝⊚————————

D efense of the idea that INH and UNIH behaviors in one- and two-year-olds were not always due to prior experiences required an examination of the possible antecedents of these behaviors in young infants. The first problem was choosing the infant behaviors that might be products of the same biology that generated INH and UNIH profiles in the second year. Research with mice and rats implied that unfamiliar objects or settings activated the basolateral amygdala which, in turn, sent projections to the central nucleus. The latter projected to targets that mediate distress vocalizations, vigorous motor actions, and an arching of the back.

If variation in the excitability of one or more nuclei of the amygdala was an important cause of INH or UNIH behavior, young infants who varied in frequency of distress cries and motor arousal to unfamiliar events might provide sensitive predictors of these profiles. Activation of the basolateral and/or central nuclei of the amygdala, which are moderated by different chemistries and neural connections, could be accompanied by one of four behavioral profiles. Some infants should display both frequent limb activity and crying to unfamiliar stimuli. A complementary group ought to display low levels of the above responses. The two other categories should show either frequent limb movements with minimal distress or frequent crying but little motor activity.

One study, which partially supported the speculations about vigorous motor acts, took advantage of the fact that newborns vary in rate and magnitude of bursts of sucking on a nipple. The infants in this study first sucked a nipple that delivered water for two minutes. The rate of sucking increased when the water was unexpectedly replaced with sugar water. This change in taste would have activated the amygdala. The newborns who displayed the largest increase in sucking rate were more likely, as two-year-olds, to display INH behaviors in unfamiliar situations than those with small increases in sucking rate [Lagasse et al., 1989]. This result enhances the credibility of the idea that variation in the vigor of motor activity to unexpected events in young infants is a potential predictor of INH and UNIH behaviors.

Nancy Snidman recruited 100 four-month-olds born to healthy, middle-class Caucasian parents. The ethnic restriction was necessary because the day care study, as well as an investigation of four-month-olds from Boston, Dublin, Beijing, or Taiwan, revealed differences between Chinese and Caucasian infants to unfamiliar events [Kagan *et al.*, 1994; Liu *et al.*, 2020].

After Nancy had filmed about 60 infants responding to innocent but unfamiliar visual and auditory stimuli, I took the films to a small room and, in a Baconian frame of mind, looked at each in order to have an idea of the range and quality of the behaviors displayed. The profiles of an initial group of infants were similar. These four-month-olds occasionally moved an arm or leg and vocalized, but they did not cry or arch their back. The next infant provided the needed clue.

This girl showed increased muscle tension to the initial presentations of colorful mobiles moving slowly back and forth in front of her face. By the fourth presentation her higher level of arousal was reflected in vigorous movements of arms and legs, crying, and several arches of the back. This infant was qualitatively different from the first group and her pattern implied a low threshold of activation in the amygdala. I knew her parents and was confident that their daughter's behaviors were not due to unusual features in the home.

About 20 percent of the 100 infants displayed vigorous limb movement, occasional arching of the back, and crying to our unfamiliar events. I learned later that many infants with this profile displayed INH behaviors during the second year. This fact motivated Doreen Arcus, a graduate student, to replicate this result with an additional 500 four-month-olds from the same class and ethnic groups. This large sample was assessed at nine, 14, 21, and 42 months.

Each four-month-old was exposed to five unfamiliar events while the mother sat at the back of the room outside her infant's gaze. After heart rate electrodes were applied and resting heart rate obtained, the infants heard the voices of women coming from a speaker baffle with a schematic face on the front speaking eight short sentences. In the second episode the examiner, standing at the back of the infant, moved mobiles with one, three, or seven colorful objects back and forth in front of the infant's face for a total of nine trials. The application of a cotton swab that had been dipped in water for one trial, followed by three applications of a swab dipped in dilute butyl alcohol comprised the third novel event. The speaker was once again placed near the infant who heard a female voice repeat the syllables *ma, pa, ga* three times at three loudness levels. Finally, the examiner popped a balloon behind the child.

The mobiles provoked the most sensitive indexes of the biology we believed were the foundations of INH and UNIH patterns. These stimuli provoked considerable variation in limb activity, crying, and arching of the back. The sentences and syllables occasionally produced a cry but less limb movement. The butyl alcohol evoked some fretting and most infants showed no response to the pop of the balloon.

About 20 percent of the combined Snidman and Arcus samples displayed frequent intervals of vigorous limb movements and crying to more than two episodes. We called these infants high reactive (HR). Although a majority of this group also arched their back, the frequency of arching had such a restricted range I decided to exclude it from the definition of an HR infant. The largest group reacted to the same events with the opposite profile. These four-month-olds, 40 percent of the sample, moved an arm or leg occasionally, but rarely cried. This group was labeled low reactive (LR). One quarter of the sample, called distressed (D), cried on two or more episodes but did not show much limb activity. The smallest group, ten percent of the sample, moved their limbs with vigor, but rarely cried. These infants were classified as aroused (A).

The Behavior Outcomes

We predicted that the HR infants would show INH behaviors to unfamiliar events and the LR group UNIH responses as older children. The incentives presented to older children changed as they matured. These incentives included the application of heart rate electrodes, encounters with robots, strangers, unfamiliar puppets, flashing lights, a toy clown, and a woman dressed in a clown's costume. Long latencies or refusal to approach an object or person, crying, and duration remaining close to the mother represented our index of inhibition. We summed the number of incentives that evoked any of these responses. Most children did not display more than one of these behaviors because none of the events was objectively dangerous or threatening. The distribution of scores suggested three groups: those with no more than one INH response, those with two or three, and those with four or more INH behaviors.

As expected, there was a major increase in INH responses between nine and 14 months. The more important finding was that the four-month-olds classified as HR had higher INH scores than LR infants at 14 and 21 months. More than half of the HR, but only ten percent of LR, had four or more INH behaviors at 14 and 21 months. The scores of the other two groups (D and A) fell between the HR and LR children. These results confirmed our hypothesis that variation in vigorous motor activity and distress to non-threatening but novel events in four-month-old infants reflected biological states that were the foundations of INH and UNIH patterns. This bias is not restricted to the laboratory. Sara Rimm-Kaufman, who visited the kindergarten classrooms of a sample of HR and LR children, found that the latter spoke, yelled, and volunteered more often than HR children. A latent class analysis of the data gathered at four and 14 months implied that HR and LR were distinct categories [Stern *et al.*, 1994].

Because not every HR infant displayed INH behavior in the second year it was reasonable to presume that the home environment was important. Doreen visited the homes of 24 HR and 26 LR infants at five, seven, nine, 11, and 13 months where she videotaped the mother-child interactions. The HR infants who had high INH scores had over-protective mothers who did not provide the child with opportunities to extinguish their cautious habits. The mothers of HR infants who displayed few INH responses did not pick up her infant as soon as she cried and, in addition, set firm limits on inappropriate actions. This evidence supports the critics of our earlier work who said that the home environment could create an inhibited or uninhibited pattern without any temperamental bias. Montaigne would have smiled on learning this result for he believed that parents who protected their child from all sources of distress and danger would sculpt a youth and adult who was unable to deal with life's usual stresses.

Readers will remember that older INH and UNIH children differed in heart rate, changes in rate, and heart rate variability. Fetuses who would become HR infants had higher heart rates than LR fetuses a few weeks before birth. And two-week-olds who became HR infants at four months had higher heart rates than LR while the mother held her sleeping infant erect [Snidman *et al.*, 1993]. Three-fourths of HR infants had both high fetal heart rates and a large sympathetic contribution to a spectral analysis of heart rate at two weeks. Most of these children were INH at 14 and 21 months. Resting heart rates obtained after four months, when the parasympathetic system exerts more control, did not always differentiate HR from LR, although magnitude of cardiac acceleration to selective events did.

The boys classified as LR displayed many spontaneous smiles during the assessments in the second year along with low resting heart rates and high heart rate variability, reflecting high vagal tone. No HR infant, boy or girl, combined UNIH behavior, frequent smiles, and a consistently low heart rate.

Independent replications remain the gold standard for the validity of all inferences. Fortunately Nathan Fox and his students at the University of Maryland found that HR infants are more likely to display INH profiles at 14 and 25 months than LR infants [Fox *et al.*, 2015].

The Assessment at 11 Years

We evaluated 237 11-year-olds who had been observed at four, 14, and 21 months. Coding of the videotapes of the initial 18 minutes of a three-hour laboratory session provided the primary behavioral evidence. These youths had to be quiet when the biological measures were gathered. We coded the number of spontaneous comments and smiles during the interaction with a female examiner. In addition, an independent observer rated, on a four-point scale, the display of all behaviors reflecting INH or UNIH during this interval.

The mothers and their preadolescents were also visited in their homes where they ranked descriptions of behavioral traits from most to least characteristic of the child. The mother's list of 28 statements referred to school grades, sociability, mood, acute emotions, and energy level. The 20 descriptions ranked by the youth emphasized emotional responses to norm violations, mistakes, worries, shyness, competitiveness, and risk aversiveness. The biological data consisted of measures of the cardiovascular system, an EEG index of hemispheric asymmetry in alpha power, event-related potentials, corrugator tension, and potentiated startle.

What We Found

Nature continued to be generous. The youths who had been HR infants were rated as more inhibited. The number of spontaneous smiles was an especially sensitive index of an LR bias. Variation in spontaneous smiling in children appears to be a heritable property [Emde and Hewitt, 2001].

The parents of LR infants perceived their 11-year-olds as highly sociable, whereas the HR youths were described as shy. However, the magnitudes of the correlations between these rankings and our laboratory observations were modest. Agreement between the two sources of evidence was only high for the youths whose behaviors were at the extremes of the distributions. Two of the youths' self-descriptions were related to their history or current behavior. The LR youths were most likely to affirm the statements "Most of the time I'm happy" and "I like to do risky things".

About one of three HR and one of two LR expressed their expected profile at 11 years. Most HR infants who were INH at 14 months failed to preserve their extremely shy, timid persona and moved to the middle of the distribution because an INH profile was not adaptive in the society in which they lived. However, many of these HR youths did possess their expected biology, which I now describe.

Hemisphere Asymmetry of Activation

Several investigators had discovered that small differences in alpha power (eight to 13 Hz) at rest between the left and right frontal lobes was modestly related to the adult traits of introversion and extroversion. Alpha power is accompanied by a state of relaxation but is replaced with higher frequency oscillations under challenge. A majority of American adults who are relaxed show slightly less alpha power in the left compared with the right frontal lobe, implying higher frequency power on the left. These adults are classified as having left frontal activation. About 25 to 30 percent have the opposite profile of right hemisphere activation. Adults who report being happy most of the time more often display left hemisphere activation. Introverts are more likely to show right frontal activation [Davidson and Fox, 1982; Davidson and Rickman, 1999]. Unpleasant events usually evoke the same asymmetry. The many papers of this measure imply that the direction of asymmetry is more likely to reflect the person's temporary state rather than a more permanent trait. That is why there is only modest stability of this measure over time.

This asymmetry in alpha power could be a product of variation in afferent inputs from the viscera to each lobe. The magnitude of brain activation caused by inputs from gut, cardiovascular system, and smooth muscle is slightly greater in the right hemisphere. Hence, children who experience frequent visceral arousal, which, if unpleasant, can be interpreted as anxiety, should show greater activation of the right frontal lobe. This prediction was confirmed for panic disorder [Wiedemann et al., 1999].

When Fox and his students reported that their HR infants who were INH at 14 months were likely to show right frontal activation, I decided to gather this measure [Calkins et al., 1996]. We affirmed their observation. HR infants who were INH at 14 and 21 months were more likely to display right frontal activation than any other group. Every HR boy who showed right frontal activation reported that the statement "I feel really bad if one of my parents said I did something wrong" described one of their distinctive traits.

Brain Stem Auditory Evoked Potential

My student Susan Woodward burst into my office one afternoon to tell me that she found a paper reporting that the magnitude of a wave form in the brain stem auditory evoked potential (BAER) was larger in patients diagnosed with panic disorder [Iwanami et al., 1997]. Maybe, she suggested, HR infants would also display this response. The BAER consists of a series of wave forms to click sounds. The first five wave forms reflect the temporal sequence of activation of the auditory nerve, cochlear nucleus, superior olive, lemniscus, and inferior colliculus. The latter, called wave 5, typically occurs six milliseconds after sound onset with a peak magnitude of six microvolts. Because the amygdala sends projections to the inferior colliculus, but not to any of the preceding sites, a larger than average wave 5 is a possible index of an excited amygdala and, therefore, a correlate of an HR pattern at four months and INH behavior in second year. Susan tested this idea.

The youths who had been HR infants displayed a larger wave 5 than LR infants [Woodward et al., 2001]. The LR youths who had left frontal activation and described themselves as "happy most of the time" had the smallest wave 5 values. The variation in the magnitude of wave 5 differentiated HR and LR infants better than any other biological measure we had gathered. It is not a coincidence that this variable is a more sensitive index of the excitability of the amygdala than the other measures. This claim finds strong support in recordings from the basolateral and central nuclei of rats selected to display high or low levels of defensive behavior to heights, light, and open alleys, events that rats find aversive. The highly defensive animals had a more excitable amygdala and larger wave 5 potentials [Nobre and Brandao, 2011].

The Cardiovascular Measures

We gathered heart rate, systolic and diastolic blood pressure, and the ratio of high to low frequency power in the cardiac spectrum while each youth lay supine. The spectrum contains two peaks. The higher frequency peak, usually about 0.2 Hz, represents the effect of breathing on heart rate mediated by the vagal component of the parasympathetic system. The lower peak, 0.05 to 0.15 Hz, is believed to reflect slower oscillations in blood pressure and body temperature [Loewy, 1990]. Greater relative power in the lower frequency peak is believed to be an indirect index of a balance between the sympathetic and parasympathetic influences that favors the former. A more excitable amygdala tips the balance toward the sympathetic branch.

A combination of the spectral ratio and resting heart rate best separated the HR and LR infants. More HR youths displayed greater power in the lower frequency peak of the spectrum and a higher heart rate. LR youths were more likely to possess the opposite pattern. These subjects also smiled more often and assigned the item "Most of the time I'm happy" to one of the top three ranks of self-descriptive statements.

We had given each child a test of auditory acuity before the wave 5 procedure to be assured that each youth could hear the clicks. This challenging test required high levels of attention for more than 30 minutes. More HR than LR displayed a linear increase in heart rate across the many trials of the test.

Event-Related Potentials

I chose to measure the magnitude of the event-related potential (ERP) that peaks at about 400 milliseconds because investigators had reported that unexpected events produce this wave form. The ERP is a time-locked, post-synaptic wave

bloodied bodies, snakes, spiders, guns, and daggers, as well as innocent scenes, and recorded the tension in the orbicularis oculi muscle whose contractions generate a blink.

The use of unpleasant scenes ignored the fact that most adults did not expect to see these pictures in a laboratory. Hence a larger blink might reflect surprise and the consequences of reflections over the reason for these odd stimuli because the eye blink to a loud sound is larger when the person is engrossed in thought or sitting in a dark room. Three of my students had found that the magnitude of the potentiated eye blink while working on anagram problems was equal to the magnitude to unpleasant pictures [Kagan and Snidman, 2004]. More troubling was the report that benzodiazepenes, which are supposed to reduce subjective reports of anxiety, did not affect the eye blink. Furthermore, the magnitude of the startle to a cue signaling the delivery of a pleasant event can be as large as the blink provoked by a cue warning of an electric shock [Bradley et al., 2018]. The corpus of evidence was sufficient to entertain a skeptical view of the assumption that a potentiated eye blink to a symbol of danger that was followed by a loud sound was a sensitive index of a fear or anxious state. Nonetheless, it seemed appropriate to gather this measure on the HR and LR youths.

But we also measured the tension in the corrugator muscle of the forehead because the tension increases when a person is engrossed in thought. We measured the corrugator tension in response to threatening and neutral events. One threatening event was a light that warned the youth of the delivery of an unpleasant air puff to the throat. The other threat consisted of nine unpleasant pictures that many psychologists had used in the past along with nine neutral scenes.

The HR youths did not have larger eyeblinks than others to either the air puff or the unpleasant pictures. However, the tension in the corrugator muscle did separate the two infant biases. The HR youths had larger corrugator values to the light signal whether it warned of a puff or guaranteed no puff because the HR were more wary during the whole procedure. This evidence casts some doubt on the popular premise that a potentiated eye blink to aversive scenes is a useful index of the ambiguous, decontextualized concepts of fear or anxiety.

An Integration

One in five HR youths combined INH behavior with high values on at least two of the differentiating physiological measures. One in three LR combined a UNIH style with low values on the biological indexes. The more important result is that less than five percent of either group developed the persona of the other temperament. Most HR or LR infants developed the persona of the average child in their society. However, each infant bias makes it difficult for the child to acquire the behaviors characteristic of the other temperament. It is hard for an HR infant to maintain the relaxed, fearless persona of an LR adolescent. Genes restrict possible outcomes; they do not determine them. Put differently, the probability that an HR infant will not become a sociable, sanguine youth is much higher than the probability that this infant will become an anxious introvert who hates parties, avoids risk, and prefers solitary activities.

The idea that a temperamental bias constrains outcomes has an analogue in the outcomes of social class. If 100 psychologists were told that each of 1000 infants was born to economically secure, well-educated parents who were affectionate and encouraged a disciplined loyalty to societal norms, they would make many more correct guesses about the traits the adults would not possess compared with the traits they did acquire. That is, the probability that few members of this sample would be sex workers, criminals, high-school dropouts, homeless, or impoverished is much higher than the probabilities attached to any personality trait, political persuasion, major in college, cognitive talent, or preferred profession. Each new fact about a person eliminates the number of possible outcomes.

Analogously, the genome of a songbird species constrains the basic form of the song, but does not determine the variations due to hearing the songs of conspecifics. A person who knew that a particular bird was a finch could confidently predict the many songs it would not sing, but less able to know the particular song it did sing [Brainard and Doupe, 2002].

12 LR boys were adolescent versions of the roles that the actor Clint Eastwood plays in films. They were rarely wary, sat with minimal muscle tension in trunk or face, spoke little, never complained about the annoyances associated with the biological measurements, and ranked the item "I'm happy most of the

time" as an appropriate descriptor of their mood. Equally important, these boys also displayed high vagal tone, left frontal activation, a small wave 5, and small magnitude N4 ERPs to the novel invalid pictures.

As was true for the younger children, a combination of biological measures best separated the two infant biases. The mean z score across seven physiological measures revealed that high scores were far more common among HR than LR subjects. The LR males had the lowest average z score while the HR boys had the highest. Even though personas changed, many HR youths who were not shy or timid possessed the biology expected of their temperament. Jung used the terms anima or animus to label the psychological properties of a temperament. He appreciated that individuals could present a persona that was inconsistent with their biology. That is exactly what we found. Temperaments make a more significant contribution to a person's dominant feeling tone than to his behaviors. The poetry of T. S. Eliot and Sylvia Plath implies possession of a temperament that made dysphoric feelings frequent.

The relative independence of the behavioral and physiological measures raises a theoretical issue. How shall we describe youths who had been HR infants and at age 11 displayed a large wave 5, high sympathetic tone, right frontal activation, and a large N4 ERP to ecologically invalid scenes, but were neither shy, timid, nor affectively subdued? The fact that some HR 11-year-olds fit this pattern implies that brain states that provoke an urge to express INH actions can be suppressed.

One insightful 11-year-old HR boy who fit this description wrote about his experience for a class assignment. Excerpts from the longer essay capture his acquired ability to control his feelings and INH persona. "I have always been more of an anxious person…It took me a very long time to realize how to cope with this heightened…nervousness. I have found that the manifestation of my anxiety can be overcome by using simple mind-over-matter techniques…For example, when I first heard about the anthrax in Washington I began to have an upset stomach. I realized that it was simply because of my anxiety that I was feeling sick. As soon as I realized that the stomachache went away. Because I now understand my predisposition towards anxiety I can talk myself out of simple fears."

Finally, it is important to remind readers who favor constructs that assume continuous processes that our evidence favors categories. The concepts HR and

LR are based on extremely high or low values on motor activity and crying at four months. The development of these children differed from the larger group who did not have extreme scores.

The Assessment at Age 15

Most of the HR and LR infants who were seen at 11 years were interviewed at home four years later. A woman with no knowledge of the adolescent's category or past behavior asked a long list of questions during a visit that lasted about three hours. In addition, each youth rank-ordered two different sets of traits that corresponded to her understanding of her personality. A coder, blind to the person's temperament, studied the filmed interviews and rated each youth on talkativeness, frequency of smiling, postural tension, small motor movements, and an overall rating of INH behaviors based on the above actions plus softness of voice and looking away from the interviewer. An independent coder agreed with the original ratings. The behaviors of HR youths matched expectations. They talked and smiled less often than LR, showed more muscle tension in body, more small movements of hands, and 61 percent were rated as INH versus ten percent of UNIH youths.

The interviewer asked about sources of worry three different times using different words and syntax. Only adolescents who had been HR as infants reported worrying about common events and settings that do not evoke anxiety in most youths. These include sitting next to a stranger on a bus or subway, going to an unfamiliar place, hearing the siren of an ambulance, and thinking about the future. One HR girl said, "I worry about the future, over not knowing what will happen next." Another HR adolescent said she did not like spring because she can never be certain of the weather on any particular day.

The two infant temperaments differed more clearly in the number of unrealistic worries than in their behavior with the interviewer. The more frequent reports of anxiety to situations that bother few 15-year-olds can be understood if we assume that these youths more often experience visceral sensations that create uncertainty. The adolescent, looking for a cause, selects the unfamiliar events in the setting, whether a stranger on a bus or an ambulance siren.

The combination of more frequent visceral inputs to the brain, a more excitable amygdala, and an unfamiliar event creates brain states in HR children and youths that can evoke thoughts about the dangers lurking in the environment. These representations generate an excessive worry over events that most youths regard as perfectly safe. Because meeting strangers is common in all cities, social anxiety can develop. This state is probably less frequent in small villages. The diagnostic category of social anxiety disorder did not appear in the manual used by American psychiatrists until 1980, a year preceded by large increases in the populations of cities over the prior 50 years. An HR temperament renders a child susceptible to worry; the setting selects the events that can provoke the worry.

A religious faith often serves to allay bouts of worry. More HR than LR attended religious services regularly and believed in God, even though there was no difference between HR and LR in the religiosity of their parents.

The youths' rankings of traits supported the behavioral data. The HR ranked the items "I am pretty serious", "I think too much before deciding what to do", and "I wish I were more relaxed" as very characteristic of them. They ranked the statement "I'm easygoing" as very uncharacteristic.

Biology

A large number of the HR and LR youths who were interviewed came to our laboratory for an evaluation of asymmetry of frontal activation, wave 5, ERP wave forms to discrepant scenes, and cardiac variables [Kagan, Snidman, Kahn and Towsley, 2007]. Most of the physiological differences found at age 11 were replicated at 15 years. More HR than LR displayed right frontal activation in the EEG at both 11 and 15 years (28 vs four percent). 40 percent of HR, but not one LR, had a large wave 5 at both ages.

ERP wave forms were gathered while subjects saw six blocks of 20 different chromatic pictures per block. Blocks one, three, and five illustrated valid scenes; blocks two, four, and six consisted of invalid pictures. As expected, all youths had larger N4 ERPS to the invalid than to the valid scenes. However, the LR showed a smaller difference between the two kinds of scenes after the first block of invalid scenes, reflecting a steep slope of habituation. The HR, by contrast, continued to show large differences in N4 wave forms between invalid and valid scenes on the final set of invalid pictures. This result implies that the excitability of the amygdala in HR youths remained high throughout all six blocks. We shall see in a later section that this shallow slope of habituation of ERPs to unexpected pictures was also found when the measure was blood flow to the amygdala. One 15-year-old girl who combined an INH profile with a large wave 5 and shallow slope of habituation of N4 to the invalid scenes told the interviewer, "I feel vulnerable when I'm with people I don't know because I don't know what to do or what to say."

We found once again that a single biological measure was a less sensitive index of temperament than patterns that combined a measure with the four-month temperament and/or behavior. Right frontal activation or a large N4 ERP, considered alone, did not predict an INH persona across all subjects. But HR youths with a high value on one or more of the biological measures were likely to be shy, timid and cautious.

The Last Evaluation

My colleague, Carl Schwartz, gathered clinical and biological measures on 135 HR and LR subjects when they were 18 years old. The sample was observed first in a laboratory that assessed blood flow (often labeled the BOLD signal which means blood-oxygenation-level dependent contrast) while the subjects saw episodes with pictures. The first episode began with repeated presentations of the same set of faces, each with a neutral expression. Then, without warning, a set of different faces appeared. The HR displayed a larger BOLD signal to the amygdala to the unexpected change in the faces [Schwartz, Kunwar, Greve, Kagan, Snidman and Bloch, 2012].

The first picture in the next procedure was a face displaying a neutral expression. This event may have led most adolescents to anticipate another set of neutral faces. However, the second face had an angry expression. As expected, the BOLD signal to the amygdala to this face was much larger among the HR, and especially among the HR who displayed many arches of the back at four months.

The evidence from the third episode affirmed the shallower slope of the N4 wave form among HR 15-year-olds to the four blocks of pictures that alternated between valid and discrepant scenes. But this time the measure was level of amygdala activity rather than an ERP wave form. The HR maintained a large BOLD signal across all four blocks of invalid scenes. These data enhance our faith in the assumption that HR infants inherit a neurochemistry or neurocircuitry that lowers the threshold of arousal in the amygdala to unfamiliar or unexpected events. Confidence in this hypothesis is aided by other facts. The modulation of the amygdala by prefrontal cortex is compromised in monkeys who show INH responses to the unexpected [Birn et al., 2014]. Second, the central nucleus of the amygdala of monkeys who display INH responses to unpredictable events is more excitable than it is in other animals [Fox et al., 2012].

Several weeks later a clinician with no prior knowledge of these adolescents administered a standard psychiatric interview. More HR than LR were diagnosed with social anxiety, depression, or generalized anxiety disorder. This result confirms a study by Chronis-Tuscano and colleagues [1999]. Although a few LR females met the criteria for one of these syndromes, few showed shallow habituation of the BOLD signal to the amygdala to the invalid scenes, frequent arching of the back at four months, or INH behavior to the many incentives at 14 and 21 months. These facts imply that an anxiety or depressive disorder, and probably most psychiatric categories for a mental illness, can originate in different blends of biology and experience [Tung and Brown, 2020]. Every diagnostic category is heterogenous in its etiology. Hence, searches for the genes that are risk conditions for each of the DSM 5 illnesses will find more than one set for every diagnosis.

Some HR adults are susceptible to being bothered by the slightest deviation from their representation of the appropriate appearance of an object or setting. They will, for example, interrupt what they are doing if they notice a crumb on a table or a lamp that is not in its ordinary location and correct the situation. These compulsive actions have different origins in biology and experience. However, one likely origin is a hyper-excitable amygdala and its projections to the basal ganglia to events that are discrepant from the person's schemata for their usual appearance. I recall reading an essay on the normally quiet, taciturn Paul Dirac who, while visiting an art museum with a friend, pointed to a tiny spot of color on a Monet painting and said, "That does not belong there."

What Have We Learned?

Fox's results on HR and LR infants and the observations of many other investigators reveal a consistency that enhances the validity of our inferences [Fox *et al.*, 2005]. This corpus removes some of the mystery surrounding the small group of young children in the Fels study who showed the avoidance of novelty characteristic of INH two-year-olds and became dependent, timid adults. Lines from T. S. Eliot's *Four Quartets* are appropriate.

> *We shall not cease from exploration*
> *And the end of all our exploring*
> *Will be to arrive where we started*
> *And know the place for the first time.*

Although HR infants can, as youths, suppress an INH persona, the biological bases for their temperament appear to be better preserved. Life circumstances exert considerable power over an adult's surface traits. An LR infant who enjoyed an affluent, affectionate childhood, excellent schools, and sufficient talent is likely to choose a career in which risky decisions are common because the risk evokes less uncertainty than it does in an adult who was an HR infant. Brain surgeon, trial lawyer, airline pilot, firefighter, or hedge fund manager are likely for these individuals. Children born with exactly the same LR bias who grew up in a poor, single-parent family in an urban neighborhood with high crime and inadequate schools are at a higher risk for a criminal career.

HR infants raised in middle-class, supportive families are attracted to professional careers in which social interaction and risk are reduced. These youths prefer to be writers, computer programmers, scientists, or mathematicians. HR infants raised in poor families and settings that select asocial adults are apt to feel inadequate and will try to find an occupation that minimizes social interaction and guarantees a secure salary. The highly competitive conditions in most industrialized nations implies a slightly better adaptation for adults who were LR infants. However, many HR infants and INH children become eminent scientists, writers, programmers, and even presidents. Chernow's biography of George Washington notes that he was a very shy child with blue eyes and a cautious adult who had an intense fear of failure [Chernow, 2010].

HR and LR are only two of the many possible temperaments that find expression in early childhood. Future scientists will discover other biases. But I suspect they will have to observe infants, not older children or adults, because environments create different personas from the same temperament as early as the second birthday. Investigators must first find a behavioral profile before searching for the physiology or genes that contribute to that pattern. The observable behaviors of most temperaments have disappeared by age four or five years. However, these invisible physiological states, like a drop of black ink that disappears in a stirred glass of glycerin, are preserved. The patterns of biology and experience that define each adult personality can be likened to a gray cloth that was so tightly woven from very thin black and white threads the color of each thread is invisible.

Chapter 5

Reflections on the Pursuits

—————————— ☙☙ ——————————

Continual reading in the sciences and history while brooding on the evidence summarized in the four prior chapters transformed hazy intuitions into three articulated beliefs. These ideas centered on the importance of examining patterns of measures, acknowledging the influences of the setting, and appreciating the problems trailing the use of language to represent observations and inferences. This chapter elaborates these beliefs. I have added personal reflections on current conditions that have a relation to one of the three beliefs. I trust readers will grant this 91-year-old, for whom this is his last book, that privilege.

Patterns

With the exception of a small number of reflexes, every psychological outcome can be the product of more than one cascade of prior events. Hence, investigators should examine relations between patterns of measures because a specific pattern often reveals a distinct causal cascade. A diagnosis of autism, based on language and social deficits, could be the product of a pattern consisting of the age of the fetus when it was infected with a particular virus or a *de novo* mutation of a particular gene that was expressed in a specific brain site. These two patterns represent different causes of the symptoms and perhaps different therapeutic regimens.

Changes in ecologies, life forms, genomes, institutions, economies, or personal histories are the product of three processes: delete, add, or rearrange a component of an existing pattern. The 38,000 human genes, protein coding and others, can assume a very large number of patterns. The consequences of a single gene depend on the pattern in which it is but one component.

That is why the popular practice of studying relations between a single predictor and a single outcome is a serious problem. Too often the investigators generalize a relation found between one pair of measures in one species to different predictor-outcome pairs in many species. The concept of anxiety is an example. Investigators who find a modest relation between variation in salivary cortisol in college students preparing a speech to give to strangers and self-reports of social anxiety often suggest that the cortisol measure is a sensitive index of all states of anxiety, including worry over illness, an aggressive attack, loss of money, a friend's rejection, or task failure, as well as a rat's reluctance to enter a brightly lit alley.

More than 70 years ago Frank Beach criticized psychologists for basing so many inferences about learning on data from laboratory-reared white rats. Psychologists prefer a small number of concepts with a broad generality over more limited concepts that specify the distinct features of the many exemplars of a broad category.

Because the validity of every conclusion depends on the source of evidence, the patterns formed from multiple sources of evidence are a better foundation for inferred processes. The excitability of the cortex depends on the balance between activity in the thalamic nucleus that transmits sensory signals to the cortex and the thalamic nucleus that inhibits these neurons [Martinez *et al.*, 2020]. No scientific discipline escapes the problems raised when one measure is treated as the index of an abstract concept. Even the rate of expansion of the universe varies with the measure. The estimate based on the temperature of the cosmos differs from the rate calculated from the brightness of galaxies and stars.

Investigators ought to measure patterns because a single feature shared by two entities or relations is a flawed guide to membership in the same category. Ripe figs and marshmallows share the quality of sweetness but differ in the critical features that define their category. Some lemurs have blue eyes but the genes for this eye color are not the genes that are responsible for blue eyes in humans. Tolstoy's novels *Anna Karenina* and *War and Peace* contain very few syllables that are unique to each novel but the patterns of syllables and, therefore, the words, differ.

The economist Paul Samuelson argued that any domain that shared the same mathematical form probably shared other properties as well. This intuition is often violated. The equations that describe the length of the hypotenuse of a right-angle triangle and the heritability equation that estimates the degree to which members of a family share the same trait are both linear additions of the squares of values. But the phenomena to which these equations refer share no other properties.

The symptoms that define each of the mental illnesses form patterns that combine the person's biological vulnerabilities, childhood events, and the local circumstances when the symptoms appeared. Most of the outcomes humans care about, for example, crime, suicide, school performance, and drug abuse, are products of patterns of conditions. The death of a parent during a child's first 18 years, an event experienced by four percent of American children, must be combined with other factors in order to predict the presence of mental symptoms in the adult [Luecken and Roubinow, 2012].

The thesis of a graduate student in my department provides a nice example of the value of examining patterns. The student wanted to discover the physical features of sounds that recruited a newborn's attention. He presented the infants with 27 sounds that varied in frequency, loudness, and rise time (time to peak intensity). After spending a year analyzing the data he was disappointed to learn that no particular frequency, loudness, or rise time recruited the infant's attention. I suggested that he look for the patterns of the three features that provoked the clearest signs of alerting. The pattern that worked best combined one particular frequency, loudness, and rise time which generated a sound that resembled the human voice [Kearsley, 1973].

One child, among more than 300 studied in the work on temperament, displayed a unique pattern from four months to 15 years. His face assumed prolonged frowns during the assessment at four months and he displayed many tantrums during the 14-month evaluation. At three years this boy expressed a rare behavior while playing with an unfamiliar boy in a playroom with both mothers present. When the other boy was inside a plastic tunnel he picked up a wooden pole and began striking the tunnel in the place where the peer was sitting. His embarrassed mother told me later that he often walked up to visitors to the home and hit them. As an adolescent he had poor grades and was ostracized by classmates. Detection of this boy's rare profile requires examining the pattern of features he displayed over time. The genetic bases for an infrequent pattern of traits are more likely to reveal causal cascades than the genomes of 10,000 adults who vary in the incidence of a broad, heterogeneous psychiatric category, such as depression, anxiety, conduct disorder, or autism [Crouch and Bodmer, 2020].

Werner and Smith [1982] studied the development of 690 children born on the island of Kauai in the Hawaiian chain. Most parents were uneducated immigrants to the island who worked on sugar plantations. The adolescents who displayed an adaptive set of traits, despite earlier adversities of prematurity, chronic illness, and/or an unpredictable home environment, possessed a pattern of four properties. These youths had the temperamental bias of a low reactive infant, were firstborn with few siblings, and were raised by better educated parents who gave the child a great deal of attention.

A moving rat's representations of different locations on a track consist of patterns of input from the medial septum to the entorhinal cortex, the latter's input to place cells in the hippocampus, and the animal's running speed [Bolding *et al.*, 2020].

Pigmentation patches, floppy or flexible ears, a less protuberant snout, and more frequent estrous in females are four defining features of tame domesticated animals compared with their wild type ancestors who are more avoidant of and more aggressive with strangers. With the exception of the patches of pigment, humans possess three of these features. However, each domesticated species possesses a different pattern of these features because of distinctive genes.

A pattern defined by the differential density of two classes of estrogen receptors mediates two kinds of human males. One class of receptors controls the development of the primary sex features of penis and testes. The other receptor blocks the development of the female features of a round face, thick lips, non-protruding chin, and minimal bodily hair. As a result, there are two kinds of men with male genitals. One has a square face, protruding chin, thin lips, and lots of body hair. The other lacks these secondary masculine features. These two classes of men should react differently to the same challenge.

The most frequent pattern in the initial 16 measures of a large number of Western musical works, classical and jazz, consisted of a single repetition of a theme (AA) followed by a different sequence (B). The opening bars of Beethoven's *Fifth Symphony* adopts this AAB pattern. A distinct wave form in EEG appears to the B event in AAB sequences, but not to AB sequences [Rozin *et al.*, 2006]. Many English poems honor an AAB pattern, including the children's poem *Jack and Jill*. The advantages of searching for patterns have not yet persuaded a majority of psychologists to adopt this strategy. Perhaps future investigators acknowledge this fact.

The Setting

The setting in which observations are gathered selects a subject's expectations, thoughts, and the probability of varied actions. The setting includes not only the specific procedure, but also the familiarity of the room and other people present. A setting is a pattern of features that awards a high probability of expression to one reaction from a set of possible alternatives. This suggestion is analogous to Darwin's claim that the local ecology selects, for each animal, one or more features from a larger collection. Frequent rainfall on a Galapagos island selects a smaller beak size in resident finch. The elevation at which the small, flowering plant called Achillea grows affects its height. A cutting that grew to 50 cm at a high elevation was only 10 cm high when planted at a medium elevation [Clausen et al., 1958].

The local setting affects the symptoms that at an-risk patient is likely to develop. The mentally ill members of a third generation of American adults who had a depressed parent or grandparent displayed a broad variety of illnesses that included substance abuse or a phobia because local circumstances affected the particular symptoms that emerged [Weissman et al., 2016]. More than 90 percent of the research on the biological and experiential correlates of a mental illness are conducted on Americans or Europeans, 15 percent of the world's population, who live in settings that differ from the majority of humans.

The number of fatal auto accidents in western American states increased from 1996 to 2017 during the five work days that followed the change to Daylight Savings Time because the sun early in the morning was now lower on the horizon than it had been for months. This slight change in the driver's perception contributed to the judgment errors [Fritz et al., 2020].

Games played between two strangers in a laboratory represent a unique setting. A number of social scientists assume that a person who rejected a $1 offer from a stranger who was given $10 in a game would turn down similar offers of ten percent of an amount when a decision was made outside the laboratory. I suspect, however, that the head of a charity who requested $1 million from a wealthy hedge fund manager would not send back a check for $100,000. Nor would a scientist who requested $3 million for a project refuse a grant of $300,000 to perform preliminary work.

The need for remote high school and college courses in 2020 due to the COVID-19 virus is accompanied by exposure to new facts and ideas in home settings with many disadvantages. These include the lack of peers who can be asked about an idea that was not understood, the inability to conduct science experiments that require expensive equipment, participate in a play, concert, or athletic event, limited access to university libraries, an inability to talk one-on-one with a teacher about a personal problem or career choice, and the distracting events that are common in many home settings.

Stanley Milgram became famous by finding that the average American adult would obey an unfamiliar examiner who told a subject to administer painful electric shocks to a stranger (who was a confederate of the examiner) in another room following an error on an assigned task. However, the setting affected the subject's conformity. Adults were less likely to administer the painful shocks when the confederate was sitting next to them and the examiner was in another room or not regarded as a legitimate authority [Milgram, 1974].

Milgram performed these studies because he wanted to understand the actions of German guards at Nazi concentration camps who killed millions of Jews. But the settings at the concentration camps were unlike the ones Milgram created. The guards knew they could be killed if they did not carry out officer orders and many believed that their behaviors served the needs of the country they loved. Milgram mistakenly assumed that an American's conformity to the request of a representative of a university to give a stranger non-fatal electric shocks applied to German guards at camps who believed that the victims they murdered were enemies of the state.

A large room with windows allowed young children to find a hidden object they failed to find in a small, windowless room [Learmonth *et al.*, 2001]. The introduction of blue lights at Japanese railway stations or a screen door placed at the edge of a subway platform reduced the incidence of suicides by a significant amount [Matsubayashu *et al.*, 2014].

Linda Bartoshuk [2014] provides an exquisite example of the power of the procedure. She wanted to find out if adults with more taste buds for the quality of sweetness experienced a sweeter taste than those with fewer taste buds. Initially, she asked adults with varying numbers of taste buds for this sensation to rate their perception of sweetness to different solutions. To her surprise, there was no relation between the two variables. Because this result was counter-intuitive she altered the procedure. The subjects now adjusted a lever that controlled the intensity of sound. They had to match the loudness of the sound to the intensity of the liquid's sweetness. The evidence from this procedure confirmed the more reasonable hypothesis that those with more receptors for sweetness did experience a sweeter sensation. One explanation assumes that the louder sound and the more intense sensation of a very sweet liquid evoked a salient feeling that was missing when the subjects rated the level of sweetness.

Neurologists during the 1960s believed that children who had difficulty detecting two brief tactile stimuli applied simultaneously to different places on the skin had a compromised brain. Elizabeth Nolan, one of my graduate students who was skeptical of this conclusion, repeated this procedure. But she prefaced the stimulations by telling the child she might be touched in two places. That simple change in procedure eliminated the failure. Almost all children reported being touched in two locations [Nolan and Kagan, 1978].

Scientists who generalize an inference from blood flow patterns in an fMRI scanner to ecologically natural settings ignore the unique features of the scanner context. Subjects are supine, motorically constrained in a narrow tube, and aware that strangers are evaluating them. These conditions create psychological and brain states that are absent when the same person encounters a similar event in a natural setting, for example, a woman with a fearful facial expression running out of a store [Lee and Siegle, 2014].

The investigators who write that oxytocin enhances social behavior and bonding do not acknowledge that this molecule and its metabolic fragments induce a relaxed state, partly by acting on GABA receptors in select brain sites [Liu *et al.*, 2015]. The setting selects the behavior and/or feeling likely to occur when one is relaxed [Cardoso *et al.*, 2016]. Bonding to a partner is selected in sexual contexts, awe if a solitary adult is staring at a star-filled sky, nostalgia if a woman reminisces on her happy adolescent years, and serenity if the person is sipping a glass of wine at the end of the day.

The status of the person with whom an adult is interacting can affect the vocal features of the latter. The voice of the television host Larry King began to resemble the vocal properties of guests who enjoyed high status in American society. No such change occurred with low status guests [Gregory and Webster, 1996]. The psychologists who rely on Mechanical Turk adults who supply evidence online do not know where a Turk informant is when he answers questions.

Richard Shweder, an anthropologist from the University of Chicago, once told a Harvard audience of an experience that confirms the power of the setting. Shweder was doing field work in the temple town of Orissa in India. Because he and his wife had invited three guests of different statuses for dinner, they had to guarantee that the food was acceptable to all three guests by having its essence removed. That spiritual transformation required Richard to go the temple and bring back food that met this criterion. After the guests had departed, Shweder's wife added some chicken to the food remaining in the bowl used during the dinner and brought it to her husband. He immediately felt disgusted because all the chicken had not come from the temple. His awareness of being in Orissa evoked a disgust he would not have felt if he were in his dining room in Chicago.

A number of adults who grew up in middle-class families in North America or Europe were persuaded by family and media to believe that they can control their fate. Hence, they feel partially responsible for disappointments or failures that are due to circumstances they cannot control. Some adults who cannot acknowledge the influence of uncontrollable events can be driven to prove to themselves that they have a measure of control over some aspect of their lives. Controlling caloric intake is often chosen as the domain to demonstrate this competence. Some members of this group become anorexic [Moisin, 2009]. These many, diverse examples should persuade investigators that the setting in which data are gathered exerts a significant influence on the evidence.

Place and Time

If we expand the definition of setting to include the features of a community in a culture during a historical era, a new collection of outcomes has to be considered. Every biography is a description of the outcomes of a person with a particular pattern of properties acting in equally particular settings. Change either the properties or the setting and the narrative changes.

The introduction of drugs to treat mental illnesses was accompanied by an extraordinary rise in the prevalence of depression, anxiety, and ADHD. Robert Whitaker suggests that many drugs intended to cure a symptom altered the brain's chemistry in ways that led to new or more severe symptoms [Whitaker, 2010]. The combination of higher levels of chemical pollutants in the environment and later age of marriage over the past 100 years in industrialized nations has increased the probability of a rare or unique change in one of the DNA bases, called a *de novo* mutation, in a father's sperm. As a result, a higher prevalence of male infertility, lower sperm counts, and serious genetic abnormalities in male offspring has been observed over the past century, including the symptoms of the severe mental disorders psychiatrists label autism and schizophrenia.

The history of our species is marked by a sequence of unpredictable changes, some due to nature, many the product of human ingenuity. Each change created a new setting that required humans in that location to apply their capacity for inference, memory, language, images, feelings, and an irresistible urge to judge select ideas and acts as morally right or wrong to alter some beliefs and behaviors in order to adapt to the new context. I have chosen four different outcomes generated by altered settings that I happen to find interesting.

Self-Conception

The properties of the members of a community affect a person's confidence in their competence at particular skills. Youths with a level of talent that is only a little better than the average in their community will know fewer more talented peers in small towns than in large cities and are more likely to participate in a school project, such as the Year Book, a school play, or an athletic team. As a result they will enjoy a feeling of superiority denied to those with the same level of skill in a city of eight million which has many youths with outstanding talents.

Eight of the 13 men who have been president since 1945, when Truman occupied the position, spent their early childhood years in small towns, not the large cities where increasing numbers of Americans live. Eisenhower, Reagan, Johnson, and Clinton, who exuded confidence and were popular, grew up in small towns where they were regarded by teachers and the community as having special abilities.

I spent my first 17 years in a central New Jersey town of 20,000 residents. Because my grades and skills placed me in the top one percent of my high school class I was selected to go to New York to participate in an important meeting. The photo that a reporter for the *New York Herald Tribune* took of me was printed in the paper the next day. I remember feeling unusually important. Had I been attending a high school in the larger city of Newark in 1946 I am quite certain that many of my peers would have had academic records better than mine and I would not have been chosen to go to the meeting.

Large cities teach most youths that there is someone better. The adolescent daughter of an educated, affluent family in Concord, New Hampshire in 1720 enjoyed a feeling of superiority. Yet her knowledge of the world and skills were inferior to those of most poor adolescents living in the same city in 2020.

Effects on Science

During the three hundred years between Galileo's discovery of spots on the moon and the introduction of quantum mechanics in the second decade of the last century, natural scientists based their inferences on observations any investigator could make with the appropriate apparatus. Quantum concepts made that impossible. No one could observe a photon or electron passing through a slit. They could only record the consequences of that event.

The physicist Percy Bridgman was one of the first scientists who appreciated the implications of this historical change. His solution was the doctrine of operationalism, which meant that the validity of every inference or meaning of a concept depended on its source of evidence, or the procedural operations that generated the observations [Bridgman, 1927]. Bridgman believed that the meaning of the diameter of a circle in centimeters when a ruler was used differed from the meaning of diameter when optical evidence provided the evidence for the diameter of an electron. This extreme position prohibits scientists from their hope of discovering that all concepts can be supported by data provided by different procedures. But the idea that the validity of a conclusion depends on the specific procedure that produced the evidence for the inference has proven correct. The dating of fossils by their amount of radioactive carbon-14 is vulnerable to error because of the burning of fossil fuels, nuclear detonations, and agricultural chemicals that leach into the soil.

The variation in the attitude toward numbers provides another example of the effect of the cultural setting. Although Mesopotamia is believed to be the society where mathematics began, the Greek advances initiated a sanctification of mathematical laws with numbers as sacred symbols. The Ionians, who were numeral mystics, labeled ten as the best number. This awe of mathematics was solidified after Galileo, Kepler, and Newton demonstrated the stunning power of equations to describe natural phenomena. Europeans, by the late 17th century, were more convinced than other societies that mathematics could reveal the order in nature.

The respect for numbers dominates economics. Robert Lucas, a distinguished economist, once declared that if a paper in this discipline did not include mathematical equations it was not economics. Too many illuminating insights fail to honor this claim. These insights include Bohr's concept of complementarity, Karl Poppers' suggestion that hypotheses should be falsifiable, and Dostoyevsky's understanding of guilt.

The demeaning attitude toward the social sciences held by many, but not all, natural scientists is based, in large measure, on the lack of lawful relations between objective measures that can be described in an equation. These scientists rarely acknowledge that only a tiny proportion of phenomena meet this demand. In most cases the investigator has to ignore many features in related phenomena. Newton's equation for the gravitational force between Earth and Sun ignores the influence of nearby planets on Earth's orbit.

The new problems the world faces in 2020 have contributed to the reduced significance of the social sciences. These threats include climate change, rising sea levels, pollution of land, sea, and air, the need for new sources of energy, the threat of a nuclear war, aging populations, and rising inequality in income and education. Each of these phenomena can be quantified with numbers and, in some cases, equations. These problems affect hundreds of millions of humans and require the efforts of scientists and engineers from many fields. By contrast, most psychologists study the problems of single individuals, such as mental illness, criminality, and academic failure, which affect far fewer people and are harder to represent in equations.

National Values

Germany provides an example of the effects of a community's distinctive properties on the minds and behaviors of its citizens. One reason the Reformation began in northern Germany, rather than France or southern Germany, is that the cities of this region had become larger by the late 15th century and their residents resented the power of the landed nobles in rural areas who sided with the Catholic bishops. Furthermore, each city state was ruled by a prince who wanted to be free of the restrictions imposed by the Catholic church. Luther's message was attractive to a large proportion of the population who disliked the Church's exploitation of Germany through indulgences. Luther's message was attractive because it awarded more power to the individual's faith and made it easier for its merchants and princes to pursue their interests.

Prussian dominance over Germany from the 16th to the 20th century was facilitated by a combination of features that was unique in Europe. This blend included unquestioned obedience to the state, a professional military run by nobles who owned large estates, a glorification of war, efficient institutions, and the Protestant values of Pietism. In addition, Germany's location between its stronger neighbors, France and Russia, during the 18th and 19th centuries rendered its citizens receptive to ideas that would differentiate their nation from their rivals. Two new concepts included the importance of Geist, meaning spirit, and a willingness among German scientists to probe more complex phenomena than French or Russian investigators. German scientists discovered the induction of tissue in the young embryo, founded the first psychology laboratory, and made the first seminal discoveries that led to quantum mechanics.

Paul Forman [2001] suggested that the shame Germans felt after losing WWI motivated large numbers of citizens to blame their physicists, who were members of the elite with international reputations. The physicists, eager to regain the public's respect, were aware of the public's attraction to a neo-romanticism that rejected the determinism and strict rationalism advocated by the nations that defeated Germany. When evidence implied flaws in the premise of strict causal relations between events, and Werner Heisenberg's algebraic matrices implied the impossibility of knowing both the location and momentum of a particle, scientists from diverse nations acknowledged the contribution of German physicists to quantum mechanics.

The Ascendance of Suffering

Changes in social conditions in the United States and Europe over the past half-century have been accompanied by a plethora of books on victims of abuse, disability, poverty, or prejudice. Most of the 50 best memoirs nominated by critics at the *New York Times* in 2019 were written by those who experienced one or more of these sources of unhappiness over many years, or were books about them. The bestselling memoir from 2000 to 2019 was *A Child Called It,* in which Dave Pelzer describes the severe abuse he experienced as a child. Books with this theme were far less frequent before 1960 when the popular memoirs or biographies were of admired adults who were not victims of abuse or physical disability, such as Andrew Carnegie, Margaret Mead, and Frank Lloyd Wright.

Most Americans who suffered during the depression of the 1930s took some responsibility for their state and did not attribute all their financial worries to one bad actor. Some contemporary Americans who are unhappy are prone to blame one person, group, institution, or their government for failing to award their welfare a priority that exceeded the welfare of the larger community. A number of poor youths who were given full scholarships to attend a prestige university are, in the summer of 2020, angry at the institution for restricting the number of students who can live on campus in order to control infections by the COVID-19 virus. This anger ignores the good reasons why the university is implementing this restriction.

What explains the increased interest in and respect for those who suffer from unhappiness? I suspect that three major conditions came together in the United States during the years after the 1969 revolt against the Vietnam war, racism, and sexism. A large number of young adults from loving, affluent families felt some guilt over their unearned privileges, many elites betrayed their obligations to the public, and women and minorities were no longer willing to accept the unfairness of their diminished status.

A mood of melancholy among many contemporary young adults in wealthy nations is fueled by the loss of faith in traditional moral ideals and the absence of an attractive replacement. The American poet Jorie Graham captured this mood in her poem *Shroud.* "I miss the toolbar. I miss the menu. I miss the place where one could push delete." [Graham, 2017, pp. 11]. Youths are bombarded with information that is devoid of a coherent meaning or ethical demands for kindness, honesty, and sacrifice.

Many young adults are reluctant to declare loyalty to an ethical standard that they invented. They dismiss the advice of Wallace Stevens. "The final belief is to believe in a fiction, which you know to be a fiction…The exquisite truth is to know that it is a fiction and that you believe in it willingly." [Stevens, 1955, pp. 391–92].

Many members of the current generation are looking for, but cannot find, a role model with moral authority to guide them to a set of ethical rules to follow. The anthropologist-writer Loren Eisley, on a train in the northeast corridor, noticed an old man slumping in his seat. When the conductor came by to collect tickets, the old man pulled out a thick wad of bills and gave them to the conductor hoping he might select his destination. The conductor picked Philadelphia.

Humans are typically happy when pursuing a goal they judge as praiseworthy, have responsibilities they accept as obligatory, and are allowed to hold illusory beliefs. A large number of youths from affluent families are apathetic because they are deprived of all three sources of vitality. College students born in the 1990s told the writer Tony Judt that it was easy for his generation because they had ideals and believed in something [Judt, 2010].

This psychological state is, at present, more prevalent in wealthy nations, such as Sweden, Austria, and the United States, than in poorer ones, such as Mexico, Ecuador, and Spain, because more young adults in the latter societies have some faith in a few moral beliefs and have more responsibilities. The suicide rates are three times higher in Austria than in Mexico.

An essay in the February 21, 2019 issue of the *New York Times* describes the unhappiness of many who work for financial firms who complain of the meaninglessness of the work, implying that their job fails to meet their understanding of morally virtuous behavior. By contrast, non-medical workers at a hospital who clean floors and earn far less than portfolio managers are less likely to report these melancholic feelings [Duhigg, 2019].

I recall my surprise one day in 1958 when I was interviewing the adults from the Fels sample. I had learned in the morning that the father of the young man I was to see that afternoon had died the previous day and I did not expect the son to keep the appointment. When he did arrive I told him that he was not obligated to come. He replied that his father taught him to honor his obligations and keeping the appointment was the ethically proper action.

I suspect that this young man's level of commitment to a moral belief is far less frequent in today's 20-year-olds. One reason for this state of affairs originates in changed parental practices. Parents of children born before the second World War taught children how to cope with the inevitable incentives for fear, anxiety, sadness, and pain. Many contemporary middle-class parents try to prevent these incentives from occurring [Stearns and Haggerty, 1991]. The new regimen deprives youths of opportunities to accept unhappiness as a fact of living and acquire coping skills.

Social Classes Create Settings

The social class of a child's family during the first dozen years is correlated with the kinds of settings the child will encounter. That is why, as I noted in Chapter 1, class of rearing is the best predictor of occupation, years of education, illness, health, longevity, sense of agency, moods, opportunities to improve one's life, access to positions of power, and conceptions of the self. The experiences associated with class are now, as in the past, powerful predictors of the above properties.

Academic achievement is typically linked to class. Most of Warsaw was destroyed by bombs during World War II. Because the rebuilt city was occupied by the Soviet Union after the war, parents varying in years of education, a sensitive index of class, lived in the same housing units. Hence, their children played together in the same yards and attended the same schools. Nonetheless, children born to parents with a college education attained better school grades than children living with parents who had not attended college. Each child's experiences in the family were the major bases for differences in the child's motivation to perfect his cognitive skills and seek high grades [Firkowska et al., 1978].

The youths in the Fels sample who were most concerned with mastery of intellectual skills came from the best educated families. The San Marcos children who attained the highest scores on our cognitive tests grew up in the small number of families who had higher status in this dirt poor, isolated village in which no adult had more than two years of schooling.

The National Institutes of Health had funded a multi-site, longitudinal study of the causes of cerebral palsy in the 1960s that enrolled thousands of pregnant mothers who gave birth to newborn infants possessing variations in their biological integrity. The mother's level of education was a far better predictor of her child's IQ scores at four and seven years than a combination of close to 100 biological measures of mother and infant [Broman *et al.*, 1975]. I was delivered by forceps that damaged my left cornea and caused so much hemorrhaging of the capillaries in my skull the obstetrician told my father that I might not survive. My parent's continual encouragement of cognitive talents compensated for this particular trauma.

Over 40 years ago two of my students measured the reading skills and IQ scores of a sample of firstborn, Caucasian ten-year-olds on whom measures of sustained attention to variations on human faces and forms had been gathered on four occasions from four to 27 months. Parental education, not the early patterns of attention, predicted reading performance and IQ for both genders [Kagan, Lapidus and Moore, 1978]. Not surprisingly, a five-year-old's willingness to wait longer for a larger reward rather than take a smaller reward immediately is more frequent among children whose parents have a college degree [Watts *et al.*, 2018].

The IQ scores of many poor, compared with middle-class, children are due more to experience than to genes. The heritability of IQ scores of children from poor families, based on degree of similarity of IQ values among the members of a family, is close to zero [Turkheimer *et al.*, 2003].

Correlations between an infant's trait and a later property are often misinterpreted as implying that an infant's inherent properties were preserved. However, in many instances the preservation is the result of remaining in a family that practiced the rearing rituals associated with their class. For example, a correlation between babbling at seven months and size of vocabulary in the same children at ten years can reflect maternal behaviors that did or did not encourage babbling and vocabulary size. A marble in a track that changes direction preserves this class of movement because of its setting and not because of an inherent disposition to alter its direction of movement.

Class of rearing accounts for far more variance in predictions of anxiety, depression, learning disorder, criminality, substance abuse, schizophrenia, bipolar disorder, or ADHD than any known set of genes. Hence, infants born with the same temperaments but raised in families differing in income and education develop distinctive traits and brain profiles [Farah, 2018]. The greater the inequality in income and education in a community, the higher the prevalence of crime, illness, and civil unrest in many nations. Income inequality in the United States and Europe declined from 1930 to 1970, and especially after World War II. But this decline was followed by a rise after 1970, implying that high or low magnitudes of inequality cycle over time.

Women from educated, affluent families who live in wealthy countries with a great deal of gender equality are unlikely to choose a STEM career because they can select biology, or the social sciences, which they believe will be more satisfying. By contrast, women from less advantaged families living in poorer nations are more likely to pick a STEM occupation because these jobs pay higher salaries than biology or the social sciences.

A millennium earlier, when 90 percent of the members of most societies were poor, shame or guilt over their compromised status was less common. These emotions are more prevalent in 2020 because the smaller proportion of poor adults in industrialized nations are taught to admire the men and women who, despite a childhood of poverty, became adults respected for their achievements. American children are reminded of Abraham Lincoln, Henry Ford, and Thomas Edison who worked hard to achieve their eminence. Knowledge of these heroes renders many less advantaged adults susceptible to a chronic self-blame that can precipitate a depressed mood.

A small number of adults who ascended to prominence despite a childhood in a poor family, live with doubts over their right to enjoy the privileges of wealth and admiration. The writer Frank Kermode, who grew up in a very poor family, was continually haunted by the thought that he did not deserve to be a respected professor at the University of Manchester [Kermode, 1995]. The Israeli writer Amos Oz describes the unhappy consequences of always feeling like an outsider living with a "constant drip-drip-drip digesting all your feelings, how it corrodes your human dignity like rust" [Oz, 2003]. On the other hand, talented outsiders are more likely to generate revolutionary ideas because they feel freer to disagree with the majority.

James Conant, a Harvard president, eminent organic chemist, and advisor to American presidents, grew up in Boston during the early decades of the last century when a small group of elite Brahmins who ran the city made the other residents feel less adequate. Conant's extreme ambition was due, in part, to a desire to gain the status the Brahmins commanded at that time [Conant, 2017]. He achieved positions of power and respect that exceeded that of the Brahmins.

Statistical Tricks

Most psychologists are aware of the contributions of class to cognitive skills, personality traits, and symptoms of mental illness. Hence, they usually rely on statistics to remove the variance attributable to class without appreciating the problems that trail this practice. Unfortunately, the use of covariance to control for class can yield mischievous results. There are several reasons for this claim.

First, the statistics that are used most often require that the magnitude of the relation between the predictor and outcome be equal across all levels of the variable being controlled and the effects of all measures are additive [Gelman and Hill, 2007]. The data do not always meet these demands. Black and Hispanic Americans, who are more likely to be poor, more often receive a diagnosis of schizophrenia than whites who report and display similar symptoms. The contribution of social class to many dependent variables, for example, a proinflammatory state, is higher than it should be for statistical analyses that remove the contribution of class to a relation between predictors and outcomes.

One pair of investigators removed the variables that are important determinants of the outcome. They removed the contribution of income, age, ethnicity, education, and employment status on judgments of life satisfaction. The results indicated that adults who lived in Louisiana were the happiest Americans [Oswald and Wu, 2010]. This conclusion is inconsistent with the fact that few Americans move to

Louisiana and a 2010 poll indicated that Louisiana residents were among the least happy Americans.

A number of respected statisticians have criticized the practice of controlling for one or more conditions in order to prove that a single predictor made a significant contribution to an outcome that was independent of class [Rohrer, 2018; Torrey and Yolken, 2018]. Donald Rubin, among the most eminent in this group, wrote me, "Very few social scientists…understand the geometry behind regression, and many interpret their results without a clear comprehension of what the method did with their data." Helena Kraemer's personal communication was harsher: "Removing (controlling for) certain variables is just crazy and more likely to be false than conclusions in which this is not done." Flawed conclusions that follow covariance manipulations are most common when sample sizes are small.

John Tukey, whom all statisticians admire, urged investigators to examine their data carefully before implementing any statistical analyses to insure that distributions are close to normal, roughly linear, and there are no extreme outliers. An unknown number of investigators do not heed Tukey's advice. The neuroscientist Nikos Logothetis affirms Tukey. "Nothing is richer than the raw data…statistical analyses all happen after this decisive first step." [Logothetis, 2020]. Alfred North Whitehead distrusted many predictions based only on the results of mathematical analyses of evidence. In a 1925 lecture at the Lowell Institute he said, "There is no more common error than to assume that, because privileged and accurate calculations have been made, the application of the result to some future is absolutely certain." [Whitehead, 1953].

Semantic Concepts

The distorting properties of language comprise the third new conviction. Animals create representations of the physical features of the objects and events they encounter. Although the form of the representation varies across phyla, it is convenient to use the term schema (pl. schemata) to refer to the brain's representations of the objects, sounds, tastes, smells, tactile, and proprioceptive cues that are processed from sensory inputs. Humans, and perhaps some animals, use schemata to create images in the mind's eye. Early humans relied on images of concrete events to communicate distances and time durations.

Humans are the only species that adds a second, qualitatively distinct representation in the form of semantic terms containing no or minimal clues to the physical features of the events named. Semantics covers an extensive domain. This section is limited to observations that are relevant to psychological outcomes. One issue involves the confounding of the semantic networks for a class term, such as mother, with the properties of a particular mother. The effect of the physical features of a word is the second theme. I deal with the former first.

Class Terms and Particulars

Semantic concepts in most languages refer to categories of objects whose exemplars possess different features in order to simplify learning and recall of the category, even though the pursuit of simplicity decreases the informativeness of the word. The class term virus names a collection of entities that contain either single- or double-stranded DNA or RNA. Single-stranded RNA viruses are more dangerous to humans because they mutate more easily. COVID-19 infection is the result of a single-strand RNA virus.

A word can refer to a specific person (a child's mother), a class (mother), or a superordinate term (human). I suggest that a question asking about a specific person can prime the network for the features of the class term. First- and second-grade children looking at 66 pairs of objects or people (no humans were used) that illustrated the antonyms strong-weak, big-small, and dangerous-safe were asked on separate occasions to pick the picture that reminded them of their mother or father. Both girls and boys selected the pictures that symbolized strength, size, and danger as more fitting for their father and the contrasting pictures for their mother. However, some of these children had mothers who were stronger, taller, or more punitive than their fathers [Kagan, Hosken and Watson, 1961]. This observation implies that the features of the class terms mother and father influenced the children's judgments of their particular parent.

This phenomenon poses a problem for investigators who rely only on questionnaires to evaluate a person's traits. Although the questions ask about the informant's traits, the subject may treat the trait as a class term. For example, the reply to the question "Do you like going to parties?" can be affected by the informant's network for parties, and not only by her past experiences at the parties she attended.

Images and Words

The images evoked by a question affect the replies. Two parents may affirm that their child is afraid of dogs, even though one parent relied on an image of her child crying and fleeing upon seeing a dog while another activated an image of the child hesitating a few seconds before petting the animal. Although the former child has a stronger fear of dogs the investigator concludes that the two are equally fearful. Different schemata and images accompany sentences in the active or passive voice despite the same semantic meaning. The sentence "The truck struck the child" is likely to evoke an image of the truck. But the sentence "The child was struck by the truck" is apt to activate an image of a child falling to the ground. The distinct images award the sentences different sense meanings. Scholars like to use the words morning star and evening star to make this point. The adjectives morning and evening evoke distinct images, even though the two terms name the same planet, Venus.

Many scholars have warned readers of the danger of assuming that a popular word probably names an observable event that evokes similar images in speakers, listeners, or readers. Virginia Woolf in a 1937 radio address said, "Words...are the wildest, freest, most irresponsible of all things...they hate everything that stamps them with one meaning...for it is in their nature to change."

The poet Adrienne Rich captured the distinction between an image and a word in a poem describing the poet's dive into the sea to see a sunken ship. "The thing I came for / the wreck and not the story of the wreck / the thing itself and not the myth." [Rich, 1973].

Historians who depend on written texts cannot know the networks of terms and images that were linked to the words men and free when Thomas Jefferson wrote "All men are created equal". Few if any contemporary adults viewing the film *The Wizard of Oz* know that Frank Baum, who wrote the book more than 100 years ago, was thinking about the loss of power and dignity among America's farmers when he created the straw man and the restricted autonomy of American men when he invented the timid lion [Kimmel, 2012]. Nor do many appreciate that Herman

Melville was probably brooding on the civil unrest in America over slavery in 1850 when he began writing *Moby Dick*. The distinguished scholar Andrew Delbanco suggested that Melville was probably thinking of John Calhoun, the anti-abolitionist senator from South Carolina, when he invented the character of Captain Ahab. The Pequod was symbolic of the state of the nation, and the whale was intended to be a symbol of the abolitionist movement [Delbanco, 2005].

The class term violence is popular among social scientists, even though the person who killed, the victim of the killing, and the reason for the act are unspecified. The networks of words and images that are linked to the 11th-century Crusaders who murdered Muslims differ from the networks of the 19th-century Americans who killed indigenous populations, Nazi guards who gassed Jews, and police officers who shot a black man running away.

Anthony Flew, a British philosopher who had been an atheist for years, began to believe in God when he was unable to generate the images representing the sequence of chance events that led to the natural world he knew [Flew, 2007]. The semantic statement declaring that the observable world is the result of chance events was insufficiently persuasive. I suggest that anyone who reflected on the many chance events that had to occur in order to hear the sound generated by tapping a wooden table with a fingertip would have the same difficulty Flew encountered. My acceptance of the Darwinian account is based on faith.

Most youths find mathematics difficult to master because they have acquired prototypic representations of contingent relations that often include images. Mathematics contains many arbitrary concepts that have never been experienced, such as imaginary numbers, infinity, and equations declaring equivalence between forms that are not identical. For example, the cardinal number four is equivalent to the square root of 16 and the square root of 16 is equivalent to $1 + 1 + 1 + 1$, but 16 and $1 + 1 + 1 + 1$ are not identical. Michael Posner reported many years ago that adults take longer (by 80 milliseconds) to detect that Aa and AA name the same letter. This observation reflects the fact that the brain first responds to the physical features of an event and later to its meaning. Because humans can create schemata and images for both observable and non-observable events they find it easy to believe that the latter exist.

Erwin Schrodinger and Werner Heisenberg had invented different equations to explain the same quantum phenomenon in the spectrum of hydrogen. Paul Dirac discovered the equation that rendered those of Schrodinger and Heisenberg mathematically equal. However, the different equations evoked different schemata and semantic networks — waves for Schrodinger and numbers in a matrix for Heisenberg — and, therefore, had distinct semantic meanings.

The dominance of language in thought is especially relevant to psychologists because many investigators brooding on their next empirical foray activate words rather than images of puzzling phenomena. They wonder about the procedures that might reveal signs of love, fear, impulsivity, or regulation of feelings rather than the reasons for variation in the time a parent spends with a child, an adult's reluctance to pick up a dead cockroach, failure to reflect on the best answer to a difficult multiple choice question on an exam, or the occasions in which an adolescent, standing in a queue waiting to enter a theatre, strikes the stranger who accidentally pushed him. The latter events, coded as schemata, are more likely to evoke a larger brain response [Pulvermuller, 2014].

Punctate and Gradual Events

The consequences of the physical features of a word are the second issue with relevance for psychology. Most humans possess associations between events that attain peak intensity in a short time, such as a siren, called punctate, and semantic terms for male. A complementary set of associations links events with a slower rise to peak intensity, such as an infant's babbling, called gradual, and femaleness [Chestnut and Markman, 2016]. Punctate and gradual stimuli are accompanied by different brain profiles [Kodera *et al.*, 1977]. Many dangerous events, such as explosions, gun shots, and sirens, are punctate. By contrast, caresses, lullabies, smiles, and sweet tastes are gradual.

Congenitally blind adults are no different from sighted children and adults in matching the word white with high pitch sounds and black with sounds of a lower pitch [Saysani, 2019]. This association may be the result of a network involving size, color, and gender. Most white objects are smaller than dark objects with similar features and women are smaller than men. Small objects make a higher pitch sound when they fall to a surface and the female voice has a higher pitch than the male voice. The link between the words white and female may be aided by the fact that white objects are usually cleaner than dark ones and cleanliness is a stereotyped feature of women. In addition, females in all cultures have fewer pigment cells making melanin which allows them to absorb more Vitamin D, an advantage when they are pregnant. As a result, women have a lighter skin color than males. Thus, a smaller size, higher pitch, and darker color are linked to the words girl, woman, and female and the opposite trio associated with the terms boy, man, and male.

Words for Brain States

The relation between names for brain states and psychological outcomes raises a thorny issue. How should we conceptualize the psychological events that emerge from prior cascades in the brain? The hope, held by many neuroscientists, that eventually brain patterns will explain and predict all psychological outcomes ignores Roger Sperry's belief that the schemata or semantic networks that originate in and emerge from one brain profile can, in turn, generate a different brain state that would not occur if the psychological phenomena had not occurred [Sperry, 1972].

Many neuroscientists use terms whose meanings require a conscious human as the noun in sentences that have neuronal assemblies as the noun agent. The verb compute is an example. No current definition of this verb allows it to be used with neurons as the noun. The class term remember has a large envelope of exemplars, each linked to distinct patterns of schemata, semantic networks, motor modules, and brain profiles.

Consider a hypothetical study in which thousands of Americans recalled where they were when they first learned of the 9/11 attack on the World Trade Center. These adults will generate different images as they try to retrieve their location and, therefore, will activate non-identical brain patterns [Gieri *et al.*, 2020]. The pattern that is shared by all subjects, probably involving parietal lobe, parahippocampal place area, and hippocampus, is only part of the pattern in each member of the sample. The shared profile cannot be treated as the basis for the retrieval of the location in each member of the sample.

This claim is supported by the blood flow patterns adults displayed as they imagined tying each of seven knots they had mastered earlier. Each person displayed a different pattern of blood flow to the imagined tying of the same knot. There was no common profile for any of the seven knots. This means that the average blood flow pattern across all subjects did not reflect the brain state of most subjects [Mason and Just, 2020]. Investigators who do not examine individual patterns risk making misleading claims about the brain bases for psychological outcomes.

Furthermore, a person automatically activates her knowledge of the origins of any unevenness in its surface appearance [Phillips and Fleming, 2020]. A raised surface on a blanket covering a bed invites different hypotheses about its cause. Adults who cannot discriminate between a painting and a photograph of a peach would have different thoughts and brain states if told that one was a photo and the other a painting.

Although knowledge of the brain pattern that precedes or accompanies a mental state or action will aid understanding, descriptions of brain states cannot, at present, replace sentences describing psychological states. Humans automatically impose a judgment of good or bad on many events. No collection of neurons responds in the same way to all the events a person evaluates as good or bad. Hence, it is reasonable to suggest that the current vocabularies for brain and psychological phenomena are incommensurable. The Nobel physicists Erwin Schrodinger and Werner Heisenberg agreed that mental phenomena cannot be reduced to or explained by quantum concepts.

Neuroscientists have not yet invented a vocabulary that adequately describes a person's brain state to an incentive at a particular moment [Logothetis, 2020]. That is why they borrow psychological words to name patterns of brain measures. Nature may be a unity, but each phase in a cascade that results in an observable phenomenon assumes a pattern missing from prior phases and often requiring a vocabulary that is inappropriate for the earlier phase. Distinct neuronal ensembles at different locations oscillate at varying frequencies to pictures of faces, figs, and flowers.

A Summary

I did not fully appreciate the importance of patterns of measures, the settings in which evidence is gathered, and the distortions the English language imposed on my conceptualizations when I was designing the Fels study in 1957. Fortunately, I acknowledged these issues when planning and analyzing the evidence on temperament. The display of inhibited behaviors at 21 months, considered alone, did not predict any variable on the later assessments. But a combination of very few inhibited behaviors in a boy who was a low reactive infant did. Because I appreciated the ambiguity of the word fear, I decided to use the term inhibited to label children who were hesitant to approach unfamiliar objects or persons.

I urge contemporary investigators to avoid my early errors by recognizing the need to quantify more than one predictor and outcome measure and to examine the different patterns of measures in the members of a sample. Investigators should stop assuming that a relation between a brain measure and detection of the direction of motion of 60 percent of the black dots on a screen can be generalized to the perceptual discrimination of direction of motion of the single deer in a scene with a dozen other animals. An acknowledgment of the features of the setting, which always includes the particular procedures administered, is equally important.

I hope more psychologists replace the habit of trying to affirm an *a priori* hypothesis with more studies that probe a puzzling phenomenon. Three such puzzles are: What brain changes precede the appearance of a moral sense in the second year? What events in the home during the first three years produce class differences in behavior? What genes contribute to the temperamental profiles I called high and low reactive? Chambers [2017] adds three additional practices that ought to be honored. Psychologists should replicate more studies, share data, and cease relying on citation indexes to evaluate the significance of an idea or procedure.

The months of working on this book honed a finer appreciation of the connections among the three pursuits. My satisfaction would be enhanced if the readers who were persuaded of the validity of one or more of my suggestions expressed their new beliefs in the design and analysis of their next investigation.

References

Antonakis, J. and Dalgas, O. (2009). Predicting elections. *Science*, 323, pp. 1183.

Arcus, D. (1989). Vulnerability and eye color. Ed. Reznick, J. S. *Perspectives on Behavioral Inhibition* (University of Chicago Press), pp. 291–297.

Arcus, D. and Kagan, J. (1995). Temperament and craniofacial variations in the first two years. *Child Dev.*, 66, pp. 1529–1540.

Arsenian, J. M. (1943). Young children in an insecure situation, *J. Abnorm. Soc. Psychol.*, 38, pp. 35–249.

Backhouse, R. E. (2017). *Founder of Modern Economics: Paul A. Samuelson* (Oxford University Press).

Barry, H., Bacon, M. K. and Child, I. L. (1957). A cross-cultural survey of some sex differences in socialization. *J. Abnorm. Soc. Psychol.*, 55, pp. 327–332.

Bartoshuk, L. (2014). The measurement of pleasure and pain. *Perspec. Psychol. Sci.*, 9, pp. 9–93.

Benenson, J. F., Tennyson, R. and Wrangham, R. W. (2011). Male more than female infants imitate propulsive motion. *Cognition,* 121, pp. 262–267.

Beyer, J. (2016). *The Force of Custom* (University of Pittsburgh Press).

Birn, R. M., Shackman, A. J., Oler, J. A., Williams, L. E., McFarlin, D. R., Rogers, G. M., Shelton, S. E. and ...... Kalin, N. H. (2014). Evolutionarily conserved prefrontal-amygdalar dysfunction in early-life anxiety. *Mol. Psychiatry,* 19, pp. 915–922.

Bloom, L. (1973). *One Word at a Time* (De Gruyter Mouton).

Bowlby, J. (1969). *Attachment and Loss* (Basic Books).

Boulding, K. A., Ferbinteanu, J., Fox, S. E. and Muller, R. U. (2020). Place cell firing cannot support navigation without intact septal circuits. *Hippocampus,* 30, pp. 175–191.

Bradley, M. M., Zlater, Z. Z. and Lang, P. J. (2018). Startle reflex modulation during threat of shock and "threat" of reward. *Psychophysiology,* 55, pp. e12989.

Brainard, M. S. and Doupe, A. J. (2002). What songbirds teach us about learning. *Nature,* 417, pp. 351–358.

Bridgman, P. W. (1927). *The Logic of Modern Physics* (Macmillan).

Broman, S. H., Nichols, P. C. and Kennedy, S. W. (1975). *Preschool IQ* (Wiley).

Brown, J. S., Kalish, H. I. and Farber, I. E. (1951). Consolidated fear as revealed by magnitude of startled response to an auditory stimulus. *J. Exp. Psychol.*, 41, pp. 317–328.

Calkins, S. D., Fox, N. A. and Marshall, P. R. (1996). Behavioral and physiological antecedents of inhibited and uninhibited behavior. *Child Dev.*, 22, pp. 523–540.

Cardoso. C., Valkanas, H., Serravalle, L. and Ellenbogen, M. A. (2016). Oxytocin and social context moderate social support seeking in women during negative memory recall. *Psychoneuroendocrinology,* 70, pp. 63–69.

Cesario, J., Johnson, D. L. and Eisthen, M. L. (2020). Your brain is not an onion with a reptile inside. *Curr. Dir. Psychol. Sci.,* 29, pp. 255–260.

Chambers, C. (2017). *The Seven Deadly Sins of Psychology* (Princeton University Press).

Chernow, R. (2010). *Washington* (Penguin Press).

Chestnut, E. K. and Markman, E. M. (2016). Are horses like zebras or vice versa? *Child Dev.,* 87, pp. 568–582.

Chronis-Tuscano, A., Degnan, D. A., Pine, D. S., Perez-Edgar, K., Henderson, H. A., Diaz, Y., Raggi, V. L. and Fox, N. A. (2009). Stable behavioral inhibition during infancy and early childhood predicts the development of anxiety disorders in adolescence. *J. Am. Acad. Child Adolesc. Psychiatry,* 48, pp. 1–8.

Chrousos, G. P. and Gold, P. W. (1999). Commentary: The inhibited child syndrome. Eds. Schmidt, L. A. and Schulkin, J. *Extreme Fear, Shyness, and Social Phobia* (Oxford University Press), pp. 193–203.

Clausen, J., Keck, D. D. and Hiesey, W. M. (1958). *Experimental Studies on the Nature of Species III: Environmental Responses of Climatic Races of Achillea* (Carnegie Institution of Washington).

Coll, C. G., Kagan, J. and Reznick, J. S. (1984). Behavioral inhibition in young children. *Child Dev.,* 55, pp. 1005–1019.

Coplan, R. J., Coleman, B. and Rubin, K. H. (1998). Shyness and little boy blue. *Dev. Psychobiol.,* 32, pp. 37–44.

Courage, M. L., Reynolds, G. D. and Richards, J. E. (2006). Infants' attention to patterned stimuli. *Child Dev.,* 77, pp. 680–695.

Cimpian, J. R., Kim, T. K. and Mc Dermott, Z. T. (2020). Understanding persistent gender gaps in STEM. *Science,* 368, pp. 1317–1319.

Conant, J. (2017). *Man of the Hour* (Simon & Schuster).

Crouch, D. J. M. and Bodmer, W. F. (2020). Polygenic inheritance, GWAS, polygenic risk scores, and the search for functional variants. *Proc. Natl. Acad. Sci.,* 117, pp. 18924–18933.

Davidson, R. J. and Fox, N. A. (1982). Asymmetric brain activity discriminates between positive and negative affective stimuli in human infants. *Science,* 218, pp. 1235–1237.

Davidson, R. J. and Rickman, M. (1999). Behavioral inhibition and the emotional circuitry of the brain. Eds. Schmidt, L. A. and Schulkin, J. *Extreme Fear, Shyness, and Social Phobia* (Oxford University Press), pp. 67–87.

Delbanco, A. (2005). *Melville* (Knopf).

DeLoache, J. S., Simcock, G. and Macari, S. (2007). Planes, trains, automobiles and tea sets. *Dev. Psychol.,* 43, pp. 1579–1586.

Diamond, A. (1990). Developmental and neural basis of memory functions as indexed by the $A\overline{B}$ and delayed response tasks in human infants and infant monkeys. *Ann. N. Y. Acad. Sci.,* 608, pp. 267–309.

Ducrest, A. L., Keller, L. and Roulin, A. (2008). Pleiotropy in the melanocortin system, coloration, and behavioral syndromes. *Trends Ecol. Evol.,* 23, pp. 502–510.

Duhigg, C. (2019). Wealthy, successful, and miserable. *New York Times.* February 21, 2019.

Emde, R. N. and Hewitt, J. K. *Infancy to Early Childhood* (Oxford University Press).

Erikson, E. H. (1963) *Childhood and Society* (W. W. Norton).

Fantz, R. L. (1964). Visual experience in infants. *Science,* 146, pp. 668–670.

Farah, M. J. (2018). Socioeconomic status and the brain. *Nat. Rev. Neurosci.,* 19, pp. 428–433.

Fox, N., Kagan, J. and Weiskopf, S. (1979). The growth of memory during infancy. *Genet. Psychol. Monogr.,* 99, pp. 91–130.

Finley, G. E., Kagan, J. and Layne, O. (1972). Development of young children's attention to normal and distorted stimuli. *Dev. Psychol.,* 6, pp. 288–292.

Firkowska, A., Ostrowska, A., Sokolowska, M., Stein, Z. and Susser, M. (1978). Cognitive development and social policy. *Science,* 200, pp. 1357–1362.

Flew, A. (2007). *There is a God* (Harper One).

Forman, P. (2001). Weimar culture, causality, and quantum theory. Eds. Galison, P., Gordin, M. and Kaiser, D. *Science and Society* (Routledge), pp. 191–226.

Fox, N. A., Henderson, H. A., Marshall, P. J., Nichols, K. E. and Ghera, M. N. (2005). Behavioral inhibition. Eds. Fiske, S., Kazdin, A. and Schacter, D. *Ann. Rev. Psychol.,* 56, pp.235–262.

Fox, A. S., Oler, J. A., Shackman, A. J., Shelton, S. E., Raveendran, M., McKay, D. R., Converse. A. K. and ...... Kalin, N. H. (2015). Intergenerational neural mediators of early-life anxious temperament. *Proc. Natl. Acad. Sci.,* 112, pp. 9118–9122.

Fox, N. A., Snidman, N., Haas, S. A., Degnan, K. A. and Kagan, J. (2015). The relations between infant reactivity at 4 months and behavioral inhibition in the second year. *Infancy,* 20, pp. 98–114.

Fox, A. S., Oler, J. A., Shelton, S. E., Nanda, S. A., Davidson, R. J., Roseboom, P. H. and Kalin, N. H. (2012). Central amygdala nucleus (Ce) gene expression linked to increased trait-like Ce metabolism and anxious temperament in young primates. *Proc. Natl. Acad. Sci.,* 109, pp. 18108–18113.

Fritz, J., Vo Phan, T., Wright, K. P. and Vetter, C. (2020). A chronobiological evaluation of the acute effects of daylight savings time on traffic accident results. *Curr. Biol.,* 30, pp. 729–735.

Gagne, J. R., Van Hulle, C. A., Aksan, N., Essex, M. J. and Goldsmith, H. H. (2011). Deriving childhood temperament measures from emotion-eliciting behavioral episodes. *Psychol. Assess.,* 23, pp. 337–353.

Gelman, A. and Hill, J. (2007). *Data Analysis Using Regression and Multilevel/Hierarchical Models* (Cambridge University Press).

Gieri, G., Leonardelli, E., Tao, Y., Machado, M. and Fairhall, L. (2020). Spatiotemporal properties of the neural representation of conceptual content for words and pictures — a MEG study. *NeuroImage,* 219, pp. 116913.

Graham, J. (2017). *Fast* (Harper Collins).

Gregory, S. W. and Webster, S. (1996). A nonverbal signal in voices of interview partners effectively predicts communication accommodation and social status perceptions. *J. Pers. Soc. Psychol.,* 70, pp. 1230–1240.

Haith, M. M. (1980). *Rules That Babies Look By* (Lawrence Erlbaum).

Hahn, T., Winter, N. R., Anderl, C., Notebaert, K., Wuttke, A. M., Clement, C. C. and Windman, S. (2017). Facial width-to height ratio differs by social rank across organizations, countries, and value systems. *PLoS ONE,* 12, e0187957.

Hassett, J. M., Siebert, E. R. and Wallen, K. (2008). Sex differences in rhesus monkey toy preferences parallel those of children. *Horm. Behav.,* 59, pp. 359–364.

Hebb, D. O. (1946). On the nature of fear. *Psychol. Rev.,* 53, pp. 259–276.

Horn, J. M., Plomin, R. and Rosenman, R. (1976). Heritability of personality traits in adult male twins. *Behav. Genet.,* 6, pp. 17–30.

Iwanami, A., Isono, H., Okajima, Y. and Kamajima, K. (1997). Auditory event-related potentials in panic disorder. *Eur. Arch. Psychiatry Clin. Neurosci.,* 247, pp. 107–111.

Judah, M. R., Shurkova, E. Y., Hager, N. M., White, E. J., Taylor, D. L. and Grant, D. M. (2018). The relationship between social anxiety and heartbeat evoked potential amplitude. *Biol. Psychol.,* 139, pp. 1–7.

Judt, T. (2010). *Ill fares the land* (Penguin Books).

Kagan, J. (1971). *Change and Continuity in Infancy* (Wiley).

Kagan, J. (1981). *The Second Year* (Harvard University Press).

Kagan, J. (1994). *Galen's Prophecy* (Basic Books).

Kagan, J. (1998). *Three Seductive Ideas* (Harvard University Press).

Kagan, J. (2008). In defense of qualitative changes in development. *Child Dev.,* 79, pp. 1606–1624.

Kagan, J. (2012). *Psychology's Ghosts* (Yale University Press).

Kagan, J. (2013). *The Human Spark* (Basic Books).

Kagan, J. (2016). *On Being Human* (Yale University Press).

Kagan, J. (2017). *Five Constraints on Predicting Behavior* (The MIT Press).

Kagan, J. (2019). *Kinds Come First* (The MIT Press).

Kagan, J., Hosken, B. and Watson, S. (1961). Child's symbolic conceptualizations of parents. *Child Dev.,* 32, pp. 625–636.

Kagan, J and Moss, H. A. (1962). *Birth to Maturity* (John Wiley).

Kagan, J. and Klein, R. E. (1973). Cross-cultural perspectives on early development. *Am. Psychol.,* 28, pp. 947–961.

Kagan, J., Klein, R. E., Haith, M. M. and Morrison, F. J. (1973). Memory and meaning in two cultures. *Child Dev.,* 44, pp. 221–223.

Kagan, J., Kearsley, R. B. and Zelazo, P. R. (1978). *Infancy* (Harvard University Press).

Kagan, J., Lapidus, D. R. and Moore, M. (1978). Infant antecedents of cognitive functioning. *Child Dev.,* 49, pp. 1005–1023.

Kagan, J., Klein, R. E., Finley, G. E., Rogoff, B. and Nolan, E. (1979). A cross-cultural study of cognitive development. *Monogr. Soc. Res. Child Dev.,* 44, pp. 1–66.

Kagan, J., Reznick, J. S. and Snidman, N. (1987). The physiology and psychology of behavioral inhibition in children. *Child Dev.,* 58, pp. 1459–1473.

Kagan, J., Reznick, J. S. and Snidman, N. (1988). Biological bases of childhood shyness. *Science,* 241, pp. 167–171.

Kagan, J., Reznick, J. S. and Gibbons, J. (1989). Inhibited and uninhibited types of children. *Child Dev.,* 60, pp. 838–845.

Kagan, J., Snidman, N., Sellers, M. J. and Johnson, M. O. (1991). Temperament and allergic symptoms. *Psychosom. Med.,* 53, pp. 332–340.

Kagan, J., Arcus, D., Snidman, N., Wang, W. F., Hendler, J. and Greene, S. (1994). Reactivity in infants. *Dev. Psychol.,* 30, pp. 342–345.

Kagan, J. and Snidman, N. (2004). *The Long Shadow of Temperament* (Harvard University Press).

Kagan, J. and Herschkowitz, N. (2005). *A Young Mind in a Growing Brain* (Lawrence Erlbaum Associates).

Kagan, J., Snidman, N., Kahn, V. and Towsley, S. (2007). The preservation of two infant temperaments into adolescence. *Monogr. Soc. Res. Child Dev.,* 72, pp. 1–75.

Kantonen, T., Karljalainan, L., Isojavarvi, J., Nuutila, P., Tvisku, J., Rinne, J., Hietala J. and ...... Nummenmaa, L. (2020). Interindividual variability and lateralization of mu-opioid receptors in the human brain. *NeuroImage,* 217, pp. 116922.

Kearsley, R. B. (1973). The newborn's response to auditory stimulation. *Child Dev.,* 44, pp. 582–590.

Kermode, F. (1995). *Not Entitled* (Farrar, Straus and Giroux).

Kimmel, M. (2012). *Manhood in America, 3rd ed.* (Oxford University Press).

Kinney, D. K., and Kagan, J. (1976). Infant attention to auditory discrepancy. *Child Dev.,* 47, pp. 151–164.

Kittilsen, S., Scholden, J., Beitnes-Johansen, J., Shaw, J. C., Pottinger, T. G., Sorensen, C., Braastad, B. O., Bakken, M. and Overli, O. (2009). Melanin-based skin spots reflect stress responsiveness in salmonid fish. *Horm. Behav.,* 56, pp. 292–298.

Kodera, K., Yamana, H., Yamana, O. and Suzuki, J. L. (1977). The effect of onset, offset, and rise decay times of tone bursts on brain stem response. *Scand. Audiol.,* 6, pp. 205–210.

Kristen, S., Sodian, B., Licata, M., Thoermer, C. and Poulin-Dubois, D. (2012). *Infant Child Dev.,* 21, pp. 634–645.

Kuhl, P. (1991). Human adults and human infants show a perceptual magnet effect for the prototypes of speech categories; monkeys do not. *Percept. Psychophys.,* 50, pp. 93–107.

Kutas, M. and Federmeier, K. D. (2011). Thirty years and counting. Eds. Fiske, S. T., Schacter, D. L. and Taylor, S. E. *Ann. Rev. Psychol.,* 62, pp. 621–647.

La Gasse, L. L., Gruber, C. P. and Lipsitt, L. P. (1989). The infantile expression of avidity in relation to later assessments of inhibition and attachment. Ed. Reznick, J. S. *Perspectives on Behavioral Inhibition* (University of Chicago Press), pp. 159–176.

Learmonth, A. E., Newcombe, N. S. and Huttenlocher, J. (2001). Toddlers' use of metric information and landmarks to reorient. *J. Exp. Child Psychol.,* 80, pp. 225–244.

Lee, K. H. and Siegle, G. J. (2014). Different brain activity in response to emotional faces alone and augmented by contextual information. *Psychophysiology,* 51, pp. 1147–1157.

Lefevre, C. E., Wilson, V. A., Morton, F. B., Brosnan, S. E., Paukner, A. and Bates, T. C. (2014). Facial Width-To-Height Ratio Relates to Alpha Status and Assertive Personality in Capuchin Monkeys. *PLoS ONE,* 9, e93369.

Levine, R. V. (2003). The kindness of strangers. *Am. Sci.,* 91, pp. 226–233.

Lewis, M. and Brooks-Gunn, J. (1979). *Social Cognition and the Acquisition of Self* (Plenum).

Littenberg, R., Tulkin, S. R. and Kagan, J. (1971). Cognitive components of separation anxiety. *Dev. Psychol.,* 4, pp. 387–388.

Liu, N., Hadj-Bouziane, F., Jones, K. B., Turchi, J. N., Averbeck, B. B. and Ungerleider, L. G. (2015). Oxytocin modulates fMRI responses to facial expression in macaques. *Proc. Natl. Acad. Sci.,* 112, pp. E123-E130.

Liu, C. H., Snidman, N., Kagan, J. and Tronick, E. (2020). Effect of maternal distress on perceptions of infant behavior may differ in Chinese-American and European-American mothers and infants. *J. Dev. Behav. Pediatr.,* 41, pp. 212–220.

Liu, S., Seidlitz, J., Blumenthal, J. D., Clasen, L. S. and Raznahan, A. (2020). Integrative structural, functional, and transcriptomic analyses of sex- biased organization in humans. *Proc. Natl. Acad. Sci.,* 117, pp. 18788–18798.

Loewy, A. D. (1990). Anatomy of the autonomic nervous system. Eds. Loewy, A. D. and Spyer, K. M. *Central Regulation of Autonomic Function* (Oxford University Press), pp. 3–16.

Logothetis, N. (2020). Q & A. *Neuron*, 201, 884–889.

Luecken, J. L. and Roubinow, D. S (2013). Differential associations between childhood maltreatment experiences and social understanding. *Dev. Rev.*, 33, pp. 1–28.

Maley, M. J., Eglin, C. M., House, J. R. and Tipton, M. J. (2014). The effect of ethnicity on the vascular responses to cold exposure of the extremities. *Eur. J. Appl. Physiol.*, 114, pp. 2369–2379.

Markman, E. M. (1992). Constraints on word learning. Eds. Gunnar, M. R. and Maratsos, M. *Modularity and Constraints on Language and Cognition* (Erlbaum), pp. 59–102.

Maroder, M., Bellavia, D., Vacca, A., Falli, M. P. and Screpanti, I. (2000). The thymus at the crossroad of neuroimmune interactions. *Ann. N. Y. Acad. Sci.*, 917, pp. 741–747.

Martinez, M. and Ballabriga, A. (1978). A chemical study of the development of the human forebrain and cerebellum during the brain growth spurt period. *Brain Res.*, 29, pp. 351–362.

Martinez, R. I., Voelcker, B., Zaltsman, J. B., Patrick, J. R., Stevens, T. R., Connors, B. U. and Cruickshank, S. J. (2020). Two dynamically distinct circuits drive inhibition in the sensory thalamus. *Nature*, 583, pp. 813–818.

Matsubayashu, M., Sawada, Y. and Ueda, M. (2014). Does the installation of blue lights on train platforms shift suicide to another installation? *J. Affect. Disord.*, 169, pp. 57–60.

Mason, R. A. and Just, J. A. (2020). Neural representations of procedural knowledge. *Psychol. Sci.*, 31, pp. 729–740.

Milgram, S. (1974). *Obedience to Authority* (Harper Row).

Mogil, J. S. (2012). Sex differences in pain and pain inhibition. *Nat. Rev. Neurosci.*, 13, pp. 859–866.

Moisin, L. (2008). *Kid Rex* (ECW Press).

Moseley, R. L. and Pulvermuller, F. (2014). Nouns, verbs, objects, actions, and abstractions. *Brain Lang.*, 132, pp. 28–42.

Muris, P., Merckelbach, H., Mayer, B. and Prins, E. (2000). How serious are common childhood fears? *Behav. Res. Ther.*, 38, pp. 217–228.

Mrzljak, L., Uylings, H. B. H., Van Eden, C. G. and Judas, M. (1990). Neuronal development in human prefrontal cortex in prenatal and postnatal stages. *Prog. Brain Res.*, 85, pp. 85–122.

Muthukrishna, M., Bell, A. V., Henrich, J., Curtin, C. M., Gedranovich, A., McInerney, J. and Thue, B. (2020). Beyond Western, educated, industrial, rich, and democratic (WEIRD) psychology. *Psychol. Sci.*, 31, pp. 678–701.

Nobre, M. S. and Brandao, M. L. (2011). Modulation of auditory evoked potentials recorded in the inferior colliculus by GABA-ergic mechanisms in the basolateral and central nuclei of the amygdala in high and low anxiety rats. *Brain Res.,* 142, pp. 20–29.

Nolan, E. and Kagan, J. (1978). Psychological factors in the face-hands test. *Arch. Neurol.,* 35, pp. 41–42.

Novey, M. S. (1975). The development of knowledge of others' ability to see. Unpublished doctoral dissertation, Harvard University.

Ogembo, J. M. (2001). Cultural narratives, violence, and mother-son loyalty. *Ethos,* 29, pp. 3–29.

Osgood, C. E., May, W. H. and Miron, M. S. (1975). *Crosscultural Universals of Affective Meaning* (University of Illinois Press).

Oswald, A. J. and Wu, S. (2010). Objective confirmation of subjective measures of human well-being. *Science,* 327, pp. 576–577.

Oz, A. (2003). *A Tale of Love and Darkness* (Harcourt).

Pelphrey, K. A., Reznick, J. S., Goldman, B. D., Sasson, N., Morrow, J., Donahue, A. and Hodgson, K. (2004). Development of visuo-spatial short-term memory in the second half of the first year. *Dev. Psychol.,* 40, pp. 836–851.

Phillips, F. and Fleming, R. W. (2020). The *Vestigial Virgin* illustrates visual segmentation of shape by cause. *Proc. Natl. Acad. Sci.,* 117, pp. 11735–11743.

Rabinowicz, T. (1979). The differentiate maturation of the human cerebral cortex. Eds. Falkner, F. and Tanner, J. M. *Human Growth* (Plenum), pp. 97–123.

Rahal, D., Huynh, V., Cole, S., Seeman, T. and Fuligini, A. (2020). Subjective social status and health during high school and young adulthood. *Dev. Psychol.,* 56, pp. 1220–1232.

Rawls, J. (1971). *A Theory of Justice* (Harvard University Press).

Reyes, L. D., Wijeakumar, S., Magnotta, V. A., Forbes, S. H. and Spencer, J. P. (2020). The functional brain networks that underlie visual working memory in the first two years of life. *NeuroImage,* 219, pp. 116971.

Rich, A. (1973). *Diving into the Wreck* (W. W. Norton).

Rosenberg, A. and Kagan, J. (1989). Physical and physiological correlates of behavioral inhibition. *Dev. Psychobiol.,* 22, pp. 253–270.

Rosenberg, A. and Kagan, J. (1987). Iris pigmentation and behavioral inhibition. *Dev. Psychobiol.,* 20, pp. 377–392.

Rohrer, J. M. (2018). Thinking clearly about correlations and causation. *Adv. Methods Pract. Psychol. Sci.,* 1, pp. 27–42.

Rozin, P., Rozin, R., Appel, B. and Wachtel, C. (2006). Documenting and explaining the common AAB pattern in music and humor. *Emotion,* 6, pp. 349–355.

Rubin, K. H., Hastings, P. D., Stewart, S. L., Henderson, H. A. and Chen, X. (1997). The consistency and concomitants of inhibition. *Child Dev.,* 68, pp. 467–483.

Sabbagh, K. (2009). *Remembering Our Childhood* (Oxford University Press).

Sakaki, M., Yoo, H. J., Nga, L., Lee, T. H., Thayer, J. F. and Mather, M. (2016). Heart rate variability is associated with amygdala functional connectivity with MPFC across younger and older adults. *NeuroImage,* 139, pp. 44–52.

Saffran, J. R. (2003). Statistical language learning. *Curr. Dir. Psychol. Sci.* 12, pp. 110–114.

Salinas, J., Mills, E. D., Conrad, E. L., Koscik, T., Andreasen, N. C. and Nopoulos, P. (2012). Sex differences in parietal lobe structure and development. *Gend. Med.,* 9, pp. 44–55.

Saysani, A. (2019). How the blind see colors. *Perception,* 48, pp. 237–241.

Schade, J. P. and Ford, D. H. (1973). *Basic Neurology, 2nd ed.* (Elsevier).

Schwartz, C. E., Wright, C. L., Shin, L., Kagan, J. and Rauch, S. L. (2003). Inhibited and uninhibited infants "grown up". *Science,* 300, pp. 1952–1953.

Schwartz, C. E., Kunwar, P. S., Greve, D. N., Kagan, J., Snidman, N. and Bloch, R. B. (2011). A phenotype of early infancy predicts reactivity of the amygdala in male adults. *Mol. Psychiatry,* 17, pp. 1042–1050.

Seedat, S., Scott, K. M., Angermeyer, M. C., Bromet, E. J., Brugha, T. S., Demyttenaere, K. and ...... Kessler, R. C. (2009). Cross-national associations between gender and mental disorders in the World Health Organization world mental health surveys. *Arch. Gen. Psychiatry,* 66, pp. 785–795.

Shweder, R. A., Turiel, E. and Much, N. C. (1981). The moral intuitions of the child. Eds. Flavell, J. H. and Ross, J. *The Emergence of Morality in Young Children* (Cambridge University Press), pp. 288–305.

Smith, S. H. Remarks on education. Ed. Rudolph, F. *Essays on Education in the Early Republic* (Harvard University Press), pp. 167–224.

Snidman, N., Kagan, J., Riordan, L. and Shannon, D. C. (1995). Cardiac function and behavioral reactivity during infancy. *Psychophysiology,* 32, pp. 199–207.

Sperry, R. W. (1972). Science and the problem of values. *Perspect. Biol. Med.,* 16, pp. 115–130.

Stearns, P. N. and Haggerty, T. (1991). The role of fear. *Am. Hist. Rev.,* 96, pp. 63–94.

Stern, H., Arcus, D., Kagan, J., Rubin, D. B. and Snidman, N. (1994). Statistical choices in infant temperament research. *Behaviormetrika,* 21, pp. 1–17.

Stevens, W. (1955). *Collected Poems of Wallace Stevens* (Faber and Faber).

Sutherland, S. (1976). *Breakdown* (Weidenfeld & Nicolson).

Theall-Honey, L. A. and Schmidt, L. A. (2006). Do temperamentally shy children process emotion differently than nonshy children? *Dev. Psychobiol.,* 48, pp. 187–196.

Thomas, A., Chess, S. A. and Birch, H. G. (1969). *Temperament and Behavior Disorders in Children* (New York University Press).

Thoresen, S., Jensen, T. K., Wentzel-Larsen, T. and Dyb. G. (2016). Parents of terror victims. *J. Anxiety Disord.,* 38, pp. 47–54.

Tomasello. M. and Vaish, A. (2013). Origins of human cooperation and morality. *Ann. Rev. Psychol.,* 64, pp. 231–255.

Torrey, E. F. and Yolken, R. H. (2018). How statistics killed the cat. *Psychol. Med.,* 48, pp. 175.

Tung, E. S. and Brown, T. A. (2020). Distinct risk profiles in social anxiety disorder. *Clin. Psychol. Sci.,* 8, pp. 477–490.

Turkheimer, E., Haley, A., Waldron, M., D'Onorio, B. and Gottesman, I. I. (2003). Socioeconomic status modifies heritability of IQ in young children. *Psychol. Sci.,* 14, pp. 623–638.

Updike, J. (1989). *Self-Consciousness* (Ballantine Books).

Walter, K. V., Conroy-Beam, D., Buss, D. M., Asao, K., Sorokowska, A., Sorokowska, P., Aavik, T. and …… Zupancic, M. (2020). Sex differences in mate preferences across 45 countries. *Psychol. Sci.,* 31, pp. 408–423.

Watts, T. W., Duncan, G. J. and Quan, H. (2018). Revisiting the marshmallow test. *Psychol. Sci.,* 29, pp. 1159–1177.

Weissman, M. M., Berry, O. O., Warner, V., Gameroff, M. J., Skipper, J., Talati, A., Pilowsky, D. J. and Wickmaratne, P. (2016). A 30-year old study of three generations of at-risk for and low risk for depression. *JAMA Psychiatry,* 73, pp. 970–977.

Werner, E. and Smith, R. S. (1982). *Vulnerable but Invincible* (McGraw Hill).

Whitaker, R. (2010). *Anatomy of an Epidemic* (Crown).

Whitehead, A. N. (1953). *Science and the Modern World* (Cambridge University Press).

Whiting, B. and Whiting, J. W. M. (1975). *Children of Six Cultures* (Harvard University Press).

Wiener, K. and Kagan, J. (1976). Infants' reaction to changes in orientation of figure and frame. *Perception,* 5, pp. 25–28.

Wilkie, J. E. and Bodenhausen, G. V. (2012). Are numbers gendered? *J. Exp. Psychol. Gen.,* 141, pp. 206–210.

Wiedemann, G., Pauli, P., Dengler, W., Lutzenberger, W., Birbaumer, N. and Buchkremer, G. (1999). Frontal brain asymmetry a biological substrate of emotions in patients with panic disorder. *Arch. Gen. Psychiatry,* 56, pp. 78–84.

Wittling, W. (1995). Brain asymmetry and the control of autonomic physiological activity. Eds., Davidson, R. J. and Hugdahl, K. *Brain Asymmetry* (Cambridge University Press), pp. 305–357.

Woodward, S. A., McManis, M. H., Kagan, J., Deldin, P., Snidman, N., Lewis, M. and Kahn, V. (2001). Infant temperament and the brainstem auditory evoked response in later childhood. *Dev. Psychol.,* 37, pp. 535–538.